Springer Series in Optical Sciences   Volume 19

Edited by David L. MacAdam

Springer Series in Optical Sciences

Edited by David L. MacAdam

Editorial Board: J. M. Enoch   D. L. MacAdam   A. L. Schawlow   T. Tamir

George A. Agoston

Color Theory and Its Application in Art and Design

With 55 Figures and 6 Color Plates

Springer-Verlag Berlin Heidelberg New York 1979

GEORGE A. AGOSTON

4 Rue Rambuteau, F-75003 Paris, France

Editorial Board

ISBN 3-540-09654-X Springer-Verlag Berlin Heidelberg New York
ISBN 0-387-09654-X Springer-Verlag New York Heidelberg Berlin

Library of Congress Cataloging in Publication Data. Agoston, George A., 1920-. Color theory and its application in art and design. (Springer series in optical sciences; v. 19) Bibliography: p. Includes index. 1. Color. I. Title.   QC495.A32 535.6   79-22190

Offset printing: Beltz Offsetdruck, Hemsbach/Bergstr. Bookbinding: J. Schäffer oHG, Grünstadt.
2153/3130-543210

Foreword

This book directly addresses a long-felt, unsatisfied need of modern color science — an appreciative and technically sound presentation of the principles and main offerings of colorimetry to artists and designers, written by one of them.

With his unique blend of training and experience in engineering, with his lifelong interest and, latterly, career in art and art education, Dr. Agoston is unusually well prepared to convey the message of color science to art and design. His book fulfills the hopes I had when I first heard about him and his book.

I foresee important and long-lasting impacts of this book, analogous to those of the epoch-making writings by earlier artist-scientists, such as Leonardo, Chevreul, Munsell, and Pope.

Nearly all persons who have contributed to color science, recently as well as formerly, were attracted to the study of color by color in art. Use of objective or scientific methods did not result from any cold, detached attitude, but from the inherent difficulties of the problems concerning color and its use, by which they were intrigued. Modern education and experience has taught many people how to tackle difficult problems by use of scientific methods. Therefore — color science.

Few artists or others who deal with color will deny that color poses difficult problems. Capable people, all well-disposed to art and the aesthetic approach, have recently added significantly to the knowledge of color and to ways of working with it. They always intended that their findings would be useful to artists and designers. Unfortunately, they have not succeeded in conveying that message, or their contributions, to those intended beneficiaries. This book by Dr. Agoston will, I think, be the bridge of color between the cultures of science and art, of which modern color scientists have dreamed but never succeeded in building.

The book is understandable by all persons, no matter what their education or experience. Everyone is interested in color. This book has a lot for everyone, no matter how little they have to do with color, nor how little their acquaintance with or interest in mathematics or physics. No equations are used. There are many graphs. They can be understood by anyone who reads newspapers or news magazines. Each graph, and its meaning for color, is explained in simple words. Yet the book is not condescending or trivial. Knowledgeable scientists will find facts and perspectives that are not found elsewhere, some of which will be new and stimulating, even to color scientists.

Rochester, September 1979   *David L. MacAdam*

Preface

My aim in this introductory text is to present a comprehensible discussion
of certain technical topics and recent developments in color science that I
believe are of real interest to artists and designers. I treat a number of
applications of this knowledge, for example in selection and use of colorants
(pigments and dyes) and light.

Early in the book I discuss what color is and what its characteristics
are. This is followed by a chapter on pertinent aspects of light, light as
the stimulus that causes the perception of color. Then the subject of the
colors of opaque and transparent, nonfluorescent and fluorescent materials
is taken up. There are sections on color matching, color mixture, and color
primaries. Chapter 6 introduces the basic ideas that underlie the universal
method (CIE) of color specification. Later chapters show how these ideas have
been extended to serve other purposes such as systematic color naming, determining complementary colors, mixing colored lights, and demonstrating the
limitations of color gamuts of colorants. The Munsell and the Ostwald color
systems and the Natural Colour System (Sweden) are explained, and the new
Uniform Color Scales (Optical Society of America) are described.

Color specification itself is a broad topic. The information presented
here is relevant in art and design, for those who work with pigments and dyes
or with products that contain them, such as paints, printing inks, plastics,
glasses, mosaic tesserae, etc., and for those who use colored lights, lasers,
and phosphors. I believe that this book can be of use as an introductory text
to others in art conservation and in industries and commerce concerned with
printing, dyeing, plastics manufacture, etc., but I have not treated their
particular technical problems and have not introduced their specialized ter-
minologies.

I have taken great care to present technical information in a simple yet
undistorted manner. No background in science or mathematics is necessary to
follow the text. Algebra is not employed, but graphs, which are indispensable
in discussing the subjects, are used in an elementary way. I believe that
readers who are familiar with graphical presentations of the sort found in
daily newspapers and news magazines will have no difficulty in understanding

the graphs in the book. In the Appendix, a page of algebraic equations is presented for the benefit of those who may wish to go further by their own efforts in treating published color data.

The text is based on information drawn principally from the current technical literature in color science, a domain that is found by many to be forbidding, especially because it extends into rather different scientific disciplines, principally psychology, physiology, and physics. Numbers within brackets, such as [2.4] and [8.26], concern citations to books and articles listed in the References Section at the end of the book. The notation [5.7,8] signifies References 5.7 and 5.8. In some cases a further distinction is made by giving the page number of a book, as [Ref.6.1, p.171].

My interest in color is that of an artist. It had its start in my early teens when I began making oil paintings. Then there was a gap in my art career when I studied and worked twenty years as a chemical engineer. Later, when I returned actively to painting, I came under the influence of artist and teacher Richard Bowman, and my use of color in painting changed radically from realistic to fauve. The development of my interest in the technical aspects of artists' materials and in the subject of color relates somehow to my training and experience in engineering. However, I can point with certainty to my physicist friend Dr. Arthur Karp as the one who kindled my interest in the basic topic of color perception.

I am indebted to Dr. David L. MacAdam for his critical reading of the manuscript, to Dr. Nahum Joel for his helpful comments on the first half of the text, and to Mr. Kenneth L. Kelly for his suggestions concerning sections of the text dealing with certain work done at the National Bureau of Standards, Washington, D.C. I am thankful to personnel of the Documentation Services of the Eastman Kodak Company at Vincennes, France, for making reference materials available to me.

Paris, September 1979   *George A. Agoston*

Contents

---

*See sample light isolation device (black page) inserted inside back cover.

1. Introduction

1.1 Color Science and Art Before 1920

Scientific aspects of the phenomenon of color perception have captured the interest of artists, musicians, and writers during the past two centuries. The German poet Goethe made many detailed observations about color perception and presented his ideas in a book entitled *Farbenlehre* (Theory of Colors) (1810) [1.1,2], which in the opinion of a prominent color authority Deane B. Judd (1900-1972) "may come to be recognized as foreshadowing, however dimly, the next important advance in the theory of color" [Ref.1.1, p. xvi].

J.M.W. Turner studied Goethe's book on color and did some compositions based on it [1.3]. His lecture notes at the Royal Academy reveal his interest as well in the work of the scientist-mathematician Isaac Newton on light.and color [1.4]. In France, Eugène Delacroix applied principles that he had learned from *De la loi du contraste simultané des couleurs* (The Principles of Harmony and Contrast of Colors) (1839) by Michel-Eugène Chevreul, chemist and director of the dye houses of the Gobelin Tapestry Works outside (now inside) Paris [1.5,6]. Neo-impressionists Georges Seurat and Paul Signac were profoundly influenced by the book *Modern Chromatics* (1879) by the American artist-physicist Ogden Nicholas Rood and applied their knowledge in their divisionist paintings [1.5,7]. In recent years, new interest in Chevreul's book has been stimulated by the artist Josef Albers (1888-1976) at Yale University [1.8,9] and by the work of Op artists who have sought ways to heighten color brilliance.

A.H. Munsell (1858-1918), artist and teacher at the Massachusetts Normal Art School (now the Massachusetts College of Art) (Boston), was particularly interested in finding an appropriate method for teaching color to children [1.10]. He devised a practical color-notation system that had a scientific basis to serve as a teaching aid. Within several decades his system assumed great importance in color science and in color technology. In 1905 Munsell complained of "the incongruence and bizarre nature of our present color names" [1.11]. Pointing out that "music is equipped with a system by which it defines each sound in terms of its pitch, intensity, and duration", he reasoned that color should "be supplied with an appropriate system based on the hue, value, and chroma of our sensations ...". The Munsell color system now serves as one important means for color specification. Other roles have been found for it. Munsell himself proposed how it may be used in choosing harmonious colors [Ref.1.12, p. 129].

1.2 Some Developments in Color Science Pertinent to Art and Design Since 1920

Denman Ross (1853-1935) and Arthur Pope (1880-1977) introduced color theory to their art and design students at Harvard University (Cambridge, Massachusetts) more than fifty years ago [1.13,14]. In that early period, Byron Culver (1894-1971) also presented the same subject at the Department of Applied Art of the Rochester Atheneum and Mechanics Institute (now the Rochester Institute of Technology) (Rochester, New York) [1.10]. Similar courses have been offered at many other art schools and departments of art and design of universities. But the examples set by Ross, Pope, Culver, and undoubtedly others were evidently exceptions. In 1942, R.B. Farnum of the Rhode Island School of Design reported, following a survey, that sometimes such subjects were treated only incidently and that too little time was allotted to them. Some entrusted to teach color theory were incompetent or insufficiently interested [1.15]. Today, undoubtedly because of the impact of new developments in science and technology, more art schools and departments of art and design are giving fuller attention to the teaching of pertinent topics in the area of color science. Art teachers and artists are writing articles about their applications of color theory and their color research [1.16-19]. The international art journal "Leonardo", which treats contemporary visual art, with full recognition given to pertinent aspects of science and technology, has presented a number of diverse articles on the subject of color.

In commerce and industry, much attention has been given to color specification. For this purpose, Munsell implemented his color system with a large set of very carefully prepared color samples. The samples were related to one another through progressive changes in visually equal steps in Hue, Value, and Chroma. For diverse applications, a number of other sample systems have been devised that are characterized by other features. Common to most such standardized systems, each of which has hundreds of samples, is the practice of assigning numbers or codes to the colors. Thus, colors matched to a standard sample are identified precisely by the corresponding number or code. This procedure is useful for communication, in commerce for example, where the use of color samples themselves would be inconvenient.

An internationally accepted method developed by the Commission Internationale de l'Eclairage (CIE) is widely employed for specifying color. It is based on the fact that the relative amounts of three standard primary colors required in a mixture to match a color can be used to identify and specify the color.

The CIE method has been applied in subsidiary ways as well, some of which are of particular interest to artists and designers. These applications refer to the simple graphical presentation that serves the CIE method. The graphical presentation provides a basis for selecting, for example, the color names for lights. It enables the prediction of the colors obtainable when two or more lights of known color are mixed. In another application, the change of color quality (hue and purity) is traced when paints are mixed or when the color of a paint film fades with time. The graphical presentation also provides a basis for selecting complementary colors. Also, the upper purity limits for colors of nonfluorescent pigments and dyes can be shown on the graph, for comparison with the purities obtained with presently available paints and inks. Furthermore, the CIE scheme is a stepping stone to another that provides for precise determination of color differences. This is of particular interest to those concerned with close control of color differences in their work and to those wishing to know specifically about the precise degree of color change.

Both the Munsell and the Ostwald color systems have been known to artists and designers for a long time. The latter system is represented by a collection of samples in the *Color Harmony Manual* [1.20], a collection provided primarily for use in design. A new collection, the *NCS* (*Natural Colour System*) *Colour Atlas* [1.21], will probably be of great importance to designers, artists, and architects. The NCS, like the Munsell color system [1.22], provides color samples selected by visual means. Of great significance is the fact that anyone with normal vision can apply the NCS method of color judgment without the use of samples and color-measuring instruments. Also, a collection of samples has recently been made available by the Optical Society of America, which provides many series of colors of equal color difference. The collection has been produced for applications in art and design as well as for study in color science.

In the English language, there is a profusion of names for colors in art, science, and commerce. Many names apply to more than one color, and many colors are labeled by more than one name. In an attempt to establish some order, one major effort has been made by the U.S. National Bureau of Standards (NBS)

and the Inter-Society Color Council (ISCC) to produce and identify a set of
about 300 easily recognized and consistent color names and to provide a dictionary that relates over 7000 currently employed color terms to the set.
Thus, for example, the term "Hooker's green", familiar to many artists, but
not all, can with the aid of the dictionary be replaced by the more universally recognizable terms "strong yellowish green" or "dark yellowish green",
depending on Munsell Value and Chroma (lightness and saturation). The ISCC-NBS
color names have been adopted by *Webster's Third New International Dictionary*
and are in wide use in commerce. But artists and designers, who were also
expected by the originators of the color-name system to derive direct benefit
from it, seem to be generally unaware of it.

The fact that there are aspects of color science that are of practical interest to artists and designers has been recognized by color experts for a
long time. In recent decades, the following persons are prominent among many
contributors to color science in areas that are particularly pertinent in art
and design: F.W. Billmeyer, Ralph M. Evans, Deane B. Judd, Kenneth L. Kelly,
David L. MacAdam, Dorothy Nickerson, W.D. Wright, and Gunter Wyszecki. Their
work has already made an impact on art conservation as practiced in museum
laboratories. It seems ironical that, although students and professional artists are rather well acquainted with earlier developments, such as the Munsell and the Ostwald color systems, many are unfamiliar with the comparatively
recent strides in color science that are not only available to them but are
also intended, in part, for their use. I hope that this book will help in
arousing their interest in this new knowledge.

2. Color: Two Concepts

2.1 What Is Color? One Answer

In everyday life, we consider color to be a *property of materials*. A ripe tomato is red, the glass of a wine bottle is green, sulfur is yellow, snow is white, and Mary's scarf is blue. We naturally appraise the colors of objects and materials in daylight. We commonly hold a piece of fabric in daylight at a window in order to judge its color. Normal daylight viewing is associated with the reported color of an object.

It is interesting that we tend to perceive colors of familiar objects, normally viewed in daylight, in an approximately unchanged way when we view them in incandescent lamp light [Ref.2.1, p. 82]. Even if snow is viewed at night under the illumination of a red lamp, it continues to be white for us. This visual phenomenon is called *color constancy*.

The notion that color is a property of things serves many practical needs in daily life, the most important of which are those of survival. It serves as well in a host of practical ways in science and technology, but not universally. For us, it is well to note that it does not always apply satisfactorily in art and in design. If, for example, someone paints a circular area green (about 5 cm in diameter) in the center of two sheets of paper, one dull red and the other neutral gray but both of the same Value, the disks will not be perceived to be the same green. This visual phenomenon is called *simultaneous color contrast*. It is clear that in order to perceive the color of an object precisely, we must view the object under prescribed conditions.

We also commonly speak of the color of light and consider color to be a *property of light*. When we look at a red traffic light, we imagine that red light is radiating to our eyes. A beam of light projected through a red glass and traversing a darkened room appears red. This observation may cause some to believe that the light is red, if they do not realize that the beam would not be visible if the air were free from dust. But, then, the red disk produced when the beam strikes a white wall deceptively convinces most of us that the light is red.

These notions about the colors of objects and of lights, like the notion that the sun rises and falls every day, are basically *incorrect*. Nevertheless, they serve us very well in daily life. Objective observations reveal that the sun is not revolving about the earth to produce sunrises and sunsets; instead the earth is spinning on its axis, one revolution every 24 hours. Similarly, objective observations show that materials and light are not colored. The scientist-mathematician Isaac Newton, discussing the subject of light in his book *Opticks* (1704), stated correctly, "Indeed, rays, properly expressed... are not coloured" [Ref.1.1, p. vii]. The scientifically correct answer to the question "What is color?" is discussed briefly in the following section.

2.2 What Is Color? Another Answer

The question "What is color?" intrigued Aristotle, but only during the past 300 years has real progress been made toward the answer. A complete answer will not be available before color perception, one of the many functions of the human brain, is fully understood.

Most of the objects that we view are *nonluminous*. They are seen generally because light that falls on them is *scattered* (diffusely reflected) to our eyes [Ref.2.2, p. 54]. The light that falls on them may come directly from luminous sources such as the sun, a glowing lamp filament, a candle flame, etc., or it may come to them *indirectly* from luminous sources after falling on other nonluminous objects such as surrounding walls, furniture, etc. Light from clouds is sunlight scattered by water droplets; light from the blue sky is sunlight scattered by molecules in the atmosphere.

When we look at an object, light that comes from it and enters an eye passes through the eye's crystalline lens and falls upon the retina, a thin membrane that covers the rear inner surface of the eye (Fig.2.1). On entering the retina, the light traverses a layer of tissue, two layers of nerve cells, and a layer of numerous light-sensitive receptor cells [Ref.2.1, p 44; Ref. 2.3, p. 26; Ref.2.4, p. 16]. There are four types of receptor cells: *cones*, of which there are three varieties, and *rods*. The absorption of light in the receptor cells results in a complex process of generating and modifying electrical potentials to produce four receptor signals that are further modified by intercellular connections and finally coded into a light-dark and two color-difference signals [Ref.2.5, p. 65]. These three coded signals are converted into electrical spike discharges by the top layer of nerve cells; they are then transmitted by optic nerve fibers to the cortex of the brain [2.6,7].

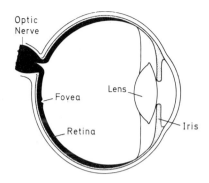

Optic
Nerve

Fovea

Lens

Retina

Iris

Fig. 2.1. Schematic diagram of the horizontal cross section of the right eye

The brain responds by producing sensations that reveal aspects of appearance
of the objects in view. Several such aspects are size, position, color, glossiness, texture, opacity, and transparency. The fact that there are some in-
terconnections between juxtaposed nerve cells, which permit light that falls
on one part of the retina to affect what is seen in another part, is cited
in explanation of visual phenomena such as simultaneous color contrast [2.6].

After stating that light "rays...are not coloured", Newton added, "There
is nothing in them but a certain power or disposition which so conditions them
that they produce in us a sensation of this or that colour" [Ref.1.1, p. vii].
Indeed, to the question "What is color?", the following answer may be given:
"Color is a sensation produced in the brain in response to light received by
the retina of the eye".

Thus, instead of saying, "That light is red", it is more precise to say,
"The color produced by that light is red". I employ the latter usage from time
to time in this book to emphasize the meaning. But usually it is less awkward
and no less effective to revert to the former.

In discussions of color perception, the term _color stimulus_ (or simply
stimulus) is generally used to refer to the light that arrives at the retina.
Sometimes a nonluminous object that scatters light, such as a red cloth, or a
luminous object that emits light, such as a red-hot soldering iron, is called
a stimulus, but the more specific term _stimulus object_ would be better [Ref.
2.1, p. 17]. Perception of a color by the brain is designated by the term _col-
or response_ (or simply _response_). It is helpful to use the words "stimulus"
and "response" later in this book where reference is made to color perception.

There is still another answer to the question "What is color?". It is an
arbitrary definition adopted by color specialists for use in colorimetry, the
measurement of color. As we shall see in Chap.6, the definition relates color
to the stimulus light and to typical eye sensitivity.

3. Perceived Colors

3.1 Isolated Colors

When we focus our eyes on a uniformly colored area on a painting, the color that we perceive is often influenced by the colors of surrounding areas. In the preceding chapter it was mentioned that this psychological phenomenon is called simultaneous contrast. Artists and designers deal with it in striving for specific color effects.

If, on the other hand, we wish to discuss or specify the precise color of a paint sample, for the sake of simplicity the sample should be considered in isolation without the influence of colors of the surroundings or in a standardized situation such as with a white or neutral gray background.

When we see a red railway signal glowing from a distance at night in the absence of other lights, we are experiencing an *isolated* or *unrelated color*. The light received solely from one such source is called an *isolated stimulus*. Often the situation of an isolated stimulus is closely approached when the surroundings are not black, if the intensity of the light (stimulus) greatly exceeds that of all of the surroundings.

Usually it is not difficult to devise a way to receive light in isolation from a luminous object. But how can the light that is scattered from an object such as a piece of paper or a sample of paint be viewed in isolation? One way is to illuminate the object in an otherwise darkened room. Another way is to view the surface through an aperture or round hole in a black panel while focusing on the perimeter of the hole. (The black page inserted inside of the back cover may be used for this purpose.) The view of the uniformly colored surface some distance behind the panel should fill the hole. Because a black panel does not return much light, practically all of the light received by the eye arrives through the hole from the surface of the viewed object. Because the hole's perimeter, not the object's surface, is in focus, the viewer gets the impression of a diffuse film-like zone. Such color perceptions are not located in depth [3.1]; they are called *film colors* or *aperture colors*.

Aspects of the appearance of objects such as glossiness, transparency, and surface texture are eliminated when surfaces are viewed in this way. Ordinarily, these characteristics would interfere in the assessment and comparison of surface colors. For example, consider the difficulty of selecting a silky fabric to match the color of a woolen fabric.

Color that is perceived to belong to an object (self-luminous, like a lamp filament, or non-self-luminous like a dab of paint or a wine bottle) is called *object color*. The color of a non-self-luminous opaque object is often more specifically referred to as *surface color*. A film color is a *nonobject* color [3.1].

3.2 Hue

Perceived colors have been found to have as many as five different character-istics or attributes [Ref.2.4, p. 94]. In the simplest case, that of isolated stimuli or film colors, there are but three attributes: *hue*, *saturation*, and *brightness* [Ref.2.4, p. 136]. Let us ask first: What is hue?

When we look at a red light, we experience the sensation of a red *hue*. It is difficult to explain just what the sensation of a red hue is, just as it is difficult to explain the sensation of bitterness or the aural perception of shrillness. It is sufficient for our purposes to say that when we utter or write the word "red", or the words "blue" or "purple", we are conveying to others the idea of a particular hue. It has been estimated that a normal eye can distinguish about 200 hues [3.2].

Perceived colors that possess a hue are called *chromatic colors*; those that do not are called *achromatic colors*. We perceive an achromatic (hueless) color when we look at a glowing daylight fluorescent lamp, for example. We also perceive achromatic colors when we view white, neutral gray, or black surfaces illuminated by such a lamp or by daylight.

It has been found that among all of the hues there are but four that are not perceived as mixtures. These are called the *unitary*, or *unique*, *hues* [Ref.2.4, p. 66]: *unitary red*, *unitary yellow*, *unitary green*, and *unitary blue*. All of the other hues are seen as mixtures of the following pairs: uni-tary green and unitary yellow (yellowish greens and greenish yellows); uni-tary yellow and unitary red (reddish yellows and oranges); unitary red and unitary blue (magentas, purples, and violets); unitary blue and unitary green (greenish blues and bluish greens).

It was mentioned in Sect.2.2 that a light-dark signal and two color-dif-ference signals are produced in the retina. This supports a hypothesis that states that three pairs of *psychological primaries*: white and black, red and

green, and yellow and blue are involved in color vision [Ref.2.4, p. 107].
The four unitary hues are basic to this hypothesis. In Sect.8.6 the use of
the four unitary hues and white and black in a practical method for judging
colors is described.

3.3 Saturation

The perception of *saturation* may be characterized as a perception of the apparent concentration of hue. To illustrate the idea, it is helpful to consider
two isolated beams of light that evoke the same hue and brightness responses
but that produce different saturation responses. Such an example may be provided by red and pink. Each response may be thought to have an achromatic
component and a chromatic component [Ref.2.4, p. 73]. The pink response has
the lower proportion of chromatic component (hue); hence, the pink color has
the lower saturation. Colors may be perceived to have 100% saturation — that
is, they have only a chromatic component. Many such colors are produced by
monochromatic light (Sect.4.3).

3.4 Brightness and Lightness

Recently, the color authority Ralph M. Evans (1905-1974) summarized in a book
his thoughts and experimental evidence concerning the attributes of perceived
color [2.4]. His discovery of the attribute brilliance is a major contribution to the science of color perception. To accommodate brilliance among the
other known attributes has required (and continues to require) a reexamination
by experts of the respective roles played by each, particularly by saturation
and by lightness. In the present brief discussion, the descriptions of the
color attributes in general conform with the concepts proposed by Evans.

Perceived *brightness* is an attribute of the illumination in which a nonisolated object is viewed [Ref.2.4, pp. 96,123]. Brightness commonly increases
when the intensity of illumination increases. More precisely stated, brightness is the "perception of the general luminance level" [Ref.2.4, p. 93] (the
term "luminance" is considered later). Brightness applies with respect to an
object only when the object is isolated and light comes to the eye from no-
where else, for example a lamp or a piece of paper illuminated by a spotlight
in an otherwise darkened room. The visual experience of brightness is commonly
described by the limits of its range: "dim" and "dazzling".

Perceived *lightness* is an attribute of nonisolated color, related color. Lightness is produced by the presence of a second stimulus or of the surroundings [Ref.2.4, pp. 136,137]. It commonly implies comparison, such as "lighter than" or "darker than" something else; it implies a perception of luminance of one color relative to the luminance of another or of the surroundings [Ref.2.4, p. 93]. We perceive lightness when we sense that more light is coming to our eyes from a piece of paper than from the brown table on which it lies.

Evans has objected to the general practice of linking lightness to brightness in considerations of the colors of nonluminous objects. Thus, a definition beginning as follows would be considered misleading: "The term 'lightness' is used in place of 'brightness' to refer to surfaces...". By such a definition, the perceptions of grayness and of darkness are incorrectly linked to brightness [Ref.2.4, p. 93]. Evans's experimental work showed that brightness and lightness are separate variables, which had also been noted by others [3.3]. Furthermore, Evans placed the perception of grayness in a separate category, that of brilliance [Ref.2.4, p. 100].

3.5 Brilliance

Brilliance, like the attribute lightness, may be perceived only when the object viewed is not isolated, for example an area of paint in a painting or a piece of glass among others in a stained-glass window. The perception of brilliance embraces two mutually exclusive aspects: either *grayness* is perceived or what Evans called *fluorence* [Ref.2.4, p. 99; 3.4], which is an *apparent fluorescence* or *negative grayness* [3.5]. To understand what is implied, let us consider a sheet of paper of a red color that possesses appreciable grayness when it is viewed in a room with normal illumination. In such cases, the light from the surroundings is more intense than that coming from the red sheet to our eyes. If, by means of a spotlight, a continuously increasing amount of light is directed onto the paper while the illumination falling on the surrounding objects remains unchanged, then the grayness of the red paper will decrease progressively and finally reach zero. At this point, the luminance of the light from the paper is still appreciably less than that of the light from the surroundings. This zero point is the separation between the regimes of grayness and fluorence (negative grayness). Then, as the spotlight illumination of the red paper is further increased, fluorence increases from zero at the zero point and the red acquires a fluorescent appearance; it is fluorent [3.4]. The fluorence continues to increase, but it finally reaches a maximum and then diminishes to zero. The maximum is reached when the lightness of the paper matches that of its surround. Above that lightness, the red appearance of the paper resembles that of a light source [Ref.2.4, p. 101].

A striking way to experience the grayness aspect of brilliance is to note the grayness of a sheet of neutral gray paper in a well-illuminated room and then the absence of grayness when the lights are turned off and the paper alone is illuminated uniformly by a white spotlight that does not "spill" on the surroundings. In the latter instance, the paper is viewed in isolation, and the color perceived is white. Similarly, a paper colored brown, which is dark yellow or orange with added grayness, appears yellow or orange when it is viewed in isolation.

It is interesting to note the difference between the perceptions of saturation and brilliance. As mentioned earlier, saturation concerns the *proportion* (concentration) of achromatic component perceived in a color. Saturation may vary from zero to 100%. Brilliance, on the other hand, concerns the perceived *amount* of grayness or of negative grayness present, both of which depend on the surrounds.

Evans's recent discovery of the perception of brilliance has thus far received little attention in the current color literature. This attribute of perceived color should be recognized by artists, designers, and others concerned with the application of color. Evans has pointed to the fact that Arthur Pope in his book *The Language of Drawing and Painting* (1949) [1.14,3.6] showed an awareness of the need for an attribute such as brilliance [Ref.2.4, p. 236]. Evans wrote: "There is no question...of the fundamental soundness of his ideas, nor of the fact that a complete rewriting of that portion of his book in terms of the four variables, hue, saturation, brilliance, and lightness as we have developed them, would remove most if not all, of the ambiguities he encountered. Carrying out such a work would be a remarkable contribution to the understanding of the arts..." [Ref.2.4, p. 235]. (Note: When related, nonisolated, colors of nonluminous objects are perceived, only four color attributes apply: hue, saturation, lightness, and brilliance [Ref.2.4, p. 137]. Brightness is assigned to the illumination.)

3.6 Color Terms

In the science of color perception, the terms "color", "hue", "saturation", "brightness", "lightness", "brilliance", "red", "blue", "achromatic", etc.,

apply to *color response* — that is, to sensation in the human brain. Used in
this sense, they are terms of psychology. In the preceding sections, the attributes of color have been described in this sense. In later parts of this
book, where color measurement and specification are described, the frame of
reference is changed. Color is linked to light (the stimulus) rather than to
the perception (the response), because precise measurements can be made on
light, relatively easily. For this reason, a new definition of color has been
adopted, psychophysical color, that is satisfyingly close to the layman's
everyday usage of the term "color". In general, there is no confusion, because the contexts wherein the terms are used provide the necessary clues.
Whenever there is a need for clarity or emphasis on the distinctions from the
other meanings of the word "color", however, use should be made of the specific terms "psychophysical color" (Sect.6.1) and "psychological color" [Ref.
3.7, p. 229].

Artists and art writers seem to employ the terms "saturation" and "chroma"
interchangeably to denote the purity of a color. The word "Chroma" is from
the Munsell color system (Sect.8.4). It is interesting that Munsell Chroma
is intended to be a correlate of perceived saturation, but Evans has shown
that it correlates more closely with a combination of saturation and brilliance [Ref.2.4, p. 168]. In art, the terms "value" (also used in the Munsell
color system) and "tone" are often employed to denote lightness [Ref.3.8,
p. 257].

The term "vividness" applied in art to colors might aptly refer to perceived brilliance. This is also suggested by the word "bright" as in "bright
red" [Ref.2.4, p. 196].

4. Light and Color

4.1 What Is Light?

What is light? A brief answer is: Light is a form of energy. Examples of other forms of energy are kinetic energy such as that transferred from the wind to the vanes of a windmill and chemical energy such as that stored in an automobile battery, available for conversion to electrical energy.

Light is a form of *radiant energy*. More precisely, light is *electromagnetic energy*, a category of radiant energy that includes X-rays, radio waves, etc. In Table 4.1 the various types of radiant energy in the electromagnetic category are presented. The whole range is called the *electromagnetic spectrum*. The relatively small range within it that represents *visible* radiant energy, light, is called the *visible spectrum*.

The term for light, "visible radiant energy", implies correctly that the visual system responds to it in the experience of seeing. We know that it does not respond to radio waves. Nor does it respond to infrared radiation, ultraviolet radiation[1], X-rays, or gamma rays, but eyesight can be destroyed by them. Only light is the *stimulus* to vision.

The portion of the sun's radiation that penetrates the earth's atmosphere consists principally of visible, infrared, and ultraviolet radiation. This "mixture" reaches the earth's surface not only directly as sunbeams but also indirectly by scattering from water droplets in clouds and by scattering produced by molecules of nitrogen, oxygen, etc., in the atmosphere. As a result, infrared, ultraviolet, and visible radiation in various proportions fall on the earth from blue, hazy, and overcast skies. The radiation emitted by a hot tungsten filament of a common light bulb (incandescent lamp) and by a fluorescent lamp contains not only visible and infrared radiation but also some ultraviolet radiation.

---

[1]A portion of the spectrum of ultraviolet radiation is sometimes called "black light" because, although it is invisible ("black") in a darkened room, it excites fluorescence in many materials that, as a result, emit visible radiation (light) (Sect.5.4).

Table 4.1. The electromagnetic spectrum. The visible spectrum occupies a small part of the electromagnetic spectrum. Wavelength is given in kilometers (km), meters (m), centimeters (cm), millimeters (mm), and nanometers (nm)

		-----10 km
		------1 km, 1000 m
	AM	
	SHORT WAVES	-------------100 m
RADIO WAVES	TV	--------------10 m
	FM	
		---------------1 m, 100 cm
	RADAR	---------------------10 cm
		-------------------------1 cm, 10 mm
	MICROWAVES	--------1 000 000 nm, 0.1 cm, 1 mm
		----------100 000 nm
INFRARED RADIATION		-----------10 000 nm
		-----------1 000 nm
VISIBLE RADIATION		
ULTRAVIOLET RADIATION		--------------100 nm
		--------------10 nm
X-RAYS		---------------1 nm
		---------------0.1 nm
		---------------0.01 nm
GAMMA RAYS		---------------0.001 nm

4.2 Wavelength and Light

Physicists tell us that electromagnetic radiation possesses a wavelike character. Indeed, a measure of waves, such as *wavelength* or *wave frequency*, is used in the measurement of electromagnetic radiation. Only wavelength is used in discussions in this book, because it is the measure most commonly found in the literature on color. The classifications in Table 4.1 have been made on the basis of wavelength.

Those who are familiar with the operation of radios know that the wavelength of radio waves is reported in meters and kilometers. But in the case of light, for which wavelengths are very much shorter, the unit of length used is commonly the *nanometer* (nm). One nanometer is equal to one millionth of a millimeter (a millimeter is one tenth of a centimeter) and to one billionth (U.S.A.) or one thousand millionth (U.K.) of a meter. Until recently, in the literature on color, the use of units called millimicrons and angstroms was common. One nanometer equals one millimicron; one nanometer equals ten angstroms.

4.3 Spectral and Nonspectral Hues

Visible radiation is commonly considered to be represented in the electro-magnetic spectrum in the wavelength range between 380 and 780 nm (Tables 4.1 and 4.2). A significant question is: What is perceived when light of a single wavelength (say 500 nm) is viewed? The answer is: Green. At 600 nm, it is reddish orange; at 470 nm, blue. Table 4.2 shows the hues perceived for radi-ation over the whole visible range. Actually the hues change gradually when the wavelength is increased continuously from 380 to 780 nm. Thus, the green-ish blue at 486 nm is more greenish than the greenish blue at 483 nm. Light of a single wavelength is called *monochromatic light*.

<u>Table 4.2.</u> The visible spectrum and the nonspectral range

	Color names for lights[a]	Wave-length range [nm]	Comple-mentary wave-length range[c] [nm]	Relative lumi-nosity (Sect. 4.7)
	Bluish Purple(bP)(Violet)[b]	−380	563c	0.0001
	Purplish Blue(pB)(Blue Violet)[b]	−430		0.0116
	Blue (B)	−465		0.075
	Greenish Blue (gB)	−482		0.15
	Blue-Green (BG)	−487		0.18
SPECTRAL	Bluish Green (bG)	−493		0.24
COLORS	Green (G)	−498		0.29
(VISIBLE	Yellowish Green (yG)	−530		0.862
SPECTRUM)	Yellow-Green (YG)	−558		1.00
	Greenish Yellow (gY)	−570		0.952
	Yellow (Y)	−575		0.91
	Yellowish Orange (yO)	−580		0.87
	Orange (O)	−586		0.80
	Reddish Orange (rO)	−596		0.68
	Red (R)	−620		0.381
	Red (R)	680	492c	0.17
	Red (R)		494c	
NONSPECTRAL	Purplish Red (pR)		498c	
COLORS	Red-Purple (RP)		528c	
	Reddish Purple (rP)		553c	
	Purple (P)		563c	
	Bluish Purple (bP)			

a Names for colored lights proposed by KELLY [7.1].
b Names employed by other authors [7.1].
c Complementary wavelength with respect to CIE ILL C.

The colors produced by monochromatic light are perceived to have 100% saturation. Yellow monochromatic light is a possible exception, in which an achromatic component is said to be perceived by some observers [Ref.2.4, pp. 73,121].

Most light that we experience is not monochromatic. For example, a beam of blue light from a colored lamp may be found to contain light over a range that may extend to over half of the visible spectrum. The major difference between a green beam and a blue beam is in the relative amounts of light contained in the green and blue wavelength regions. For example, a green beam has typically relatively larger amounts of light in the green region, from 500 to 550 nm, and a blue beam has larger amounts in the blue region, from 400 to 530 nm. The particular hue that is perceived is due partly to the predominance of energy in a wavelength region and partly to the brightness sensitivity of the eye (Sect.4.7). The light present at other wavelengths can result in a neutralizing effect that causes dilution and, hence, lower saturation.

When a beam of light from a lamp or from the sun is passed into an optical device called a *monochromator*, components of the radiation can be isolated in *wavelength intervals* or *bands*, for example 10 nm wavelength intervals. Thus a wavelength interval of light of 500-510 nm can be separated and projected onto a screen. In a device called a *spectroradiometer* [Ref.2.2, p. 11], each wavelength interval of light over the whole visible range from 380 to 780 nm can be separated and the amount of energy in the intervals measured. In this way it is possible to compare the compositions of light from different sources, such as those of light from green and blue lamps.

The hues represented by monochromatic radiation from 380 to 780 nm are those that are present in the sun's spectrum, a common example of which is provided by a rainbow. Those hues are called the *spectral hues*; all colors, regardless of saturation (the colors in a rainbow have low saturation), perceived to have a spectral hue, are called *spectral colors*. But spectral hues are not the only ones that we commonly experience. There are also purple, purplish red, and a range of neighboring red hues that are not present in the sun's spectrum or in the spectrum of any source. Such hues are called *nonspectral hues*; colors having these hues are called *nonspectral colors*. Monochromatic radiation cannot produce nonspectral colors, but mixtures of two or more beams of monochromatic radiation of different wavelength can. Nonspectral colors of essentially 100% saturation can be produced by combinations of, for example, monochromatic light of wavelength 680 nm (red) and monochromatic light of wavelength 420 nm (bluish purple). Nonspectral colors of lower saturation are produced by beams that commonly contain light from most of the spectral range but with predominant amounts from the red and blue regions. Comprehension of the wavelength composition of light is aided very much by graphical presentations, which are discussed in Sect.4.5.

4.4 Light from Lasers

Relatively recently, light sources called *lasers* have become commercially available. They can be used to produce monochromatic light. Because their light beams, or *laser beams* as they are called, commonly have radiation densities that greatly exceed those in light beams from ordinary lamps and in sunbeams, lasers are finding diverse uses in science, medicine, and technology. A laser beam consists of light in parallel rays and of one, two, or several wavelengths. The light is said to be coherent, which means that wave trains of energy are in step with each other, not out of step (out of phase) as in ordinary light.

Various media are used for the production of laser beams: crystals, glasses, gases (for example, argon, krypton, and mixtures of helium and neon), and solutions of dyes. Some *gas lasers* have been used as light sources in light art. Frequently, a helium-neon laser is employed, which produces a beam of monochromatic red light (632.8 nm) [4.1,2]. Also, the use of an argon-gas laser with a beam containing principally two wavelengths (488.0 nm, blue-green, and 514.5 nm, green) has been reported [4.1]. In the latter case, light of the two wavelengths was separated by use of a diffraction grating to produce two monochromatic beams of different colors [4.3].

Dye lasers can produce beams at any desired wavelength between 400 and 750 nm [4.4-6]. At their present stage of development, dye lasers are exclusively pulsed devices; they require auxiliary equipment (an electronic flash tube or an additional laser) to drive them [4.7]. Of particular interest is the tunability of dye lasers, which permits the production of monochromatic light of any wavelength within ranges of 30 to 50 nm or more [4.5].

In the selection of lasers, very careful consideration must be given to their safety hazards. The output from a laser at power levels below 5 milli-watts is deemed to be safe. But, even then, certain precautions must be taken to ensure absolute safety [Ref.4.8, p. 7].

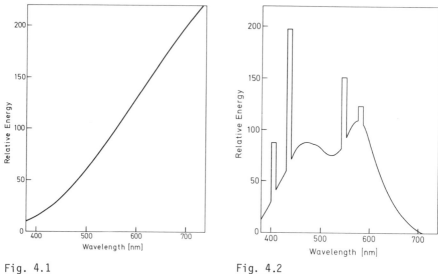

Fig. 4.1

Fig. 4.2

Fig. 4.1. Wavelength composition of light from a tungsten-filament lamp (typified by CIE ILL A, Sect.4.6). Relative spectral-energy distribution curve

Fig. 4.2. Wavelength composition of light from a daylight fluorescent lamp. Typical relative spectral-energy distribution curve. (Based on data of C.W. JEROME reported in [Ref.3.7, p.37])

4.5 Light from the Sun and from Lamps

As mentioned in Sect.4.3, most light that we experience is not monochromatic; an example of two typical green and blue lights was cited. It is characteristic among the various light sources (the sun, a candle flame, an incandescent light bulb, a fluorescent lamp, etc.) that there are appreciable differences in the distributions of relative amounts of light emitted over the range from 380 to 780 nm. Light from an incandescent light bulb contains a relatively greater amount of radiation at 650 nm than does light from a daylight fluorescent lamp. At 450 nm, the relative amount of radiation is greater from the fluorescent lamp. The *wavelength composition* of the light represents the relative amounts of light or *relative radiant energy* emitted within wavelength intervals (say 10 nm intervals) over the whole visible range.

The wavelength composition of light may be determined by use of a spectroradiometer, as mentioned above. The wavelength composition plotted as relative radiant energy versus wavelength is called a *relative spectral-energy distribution curve*. Typical curves for light from an incandescent bulb and from a fluorescent lamp are shown in Figs.4.1 and 4.2. Comparison of the two curves reveals the relatively greater amount of radiation at 450 nm for the fluorescent lamp and at 650 nm for the incandescent light bulb. From the shapes of the two curves near 380 nm, it is clear that both extend below 380 nm and, hence, that the radiation from such fluorescent and incandescent lamps includes ultraviolet radiation.

The spectral-energy distribution curve for the daylight-fluorescent-lamp radiation shows four vertical bars (Fig.4.2). Each represents a wavelength interval, 10 nm wide, within which there is a tall sharp peak or jump of radiation that is characteristic of mercury vapor, which is in the tube. The smooth, continuous portions of the curve represent the radiation contributed by the phosphors in the lamp. The jumps, four monochromatic emissions from the mercury, are superimposed on, or mixed with, the diffuse multicomponent contribution from the phosphors. A precise indication of the actual peaks would serve no useful purpose in the discussion of color. The bars shown represent accurately the energy averaged over the 10 nm wavelength intervals.

Figure 4.3 shows typical relative spectral-energy distribution curves for direct sunlight (I) and for north-sky light received on a 45° plane (II) at Cleveland, Ohio [4.9]. These two curves may be compared with a standard curve CIE ILL D_{65} (Sect.4.6), which represents a typical phase of daylight. North-sky light in the northern hemisphere is judged to be "cooler" than direct sunlight, because it contains a greater proportion of light at shorter wavelengths (blue) and a lower proportion of light at longer wavelengths (red). Also shown in Fig.4.3 is a horizontal dashed line (E) which has been added to represent an equal-energy distribution — that is, a distribution in which the relative energy does not vary with wavelength. This distribution serves as an arbitrary definition of a white light for purposes discussed later (Sect.6.3). Generally it is of interest because it can be regarded as a kind of intermediate representation for white light between the extremes of north-sky light and ordinary incandescent-lamp illumination [Ref.2.4, p. 52].

In Figs.4.1 and 4.2, the curves pass through the point that represents a relative radiant energy of 100 arbitrary units at 560 nm — that is, the light from each source is assumed to have an energy level of 100 at 560 nm; the energy at any other wavelength is indicated relative to it. This is done to facilitate comparison of light from different sources at differing intensity levels, such as sunlight and light from a 40-watt lamp. They are placed on the same basis, permitting judgment of the relative quality of "coolness", for example.

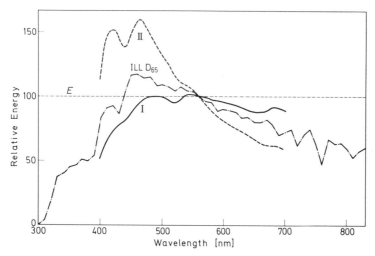

Fig. 4.3. Wavelength composition of direct sunlight (I) and north-sky light (II). The curves for CIE ILL D_{65} (Sect.4.6) and the equal-energy distribution E are shown for comparison. Relative spectral-energy distribution curves. (Curves I and II are based on observations in Cleveland, Ohio, reported in [4.9])

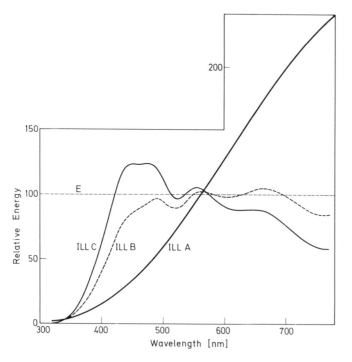

Fig. 4.4. CIE Illuminants (CIE ILL A, CIE ILL B and CIE ILL C) and the equal-energy distribution (E). Relative spectral-energy distribution curves

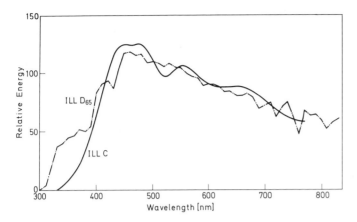

Fig. 4.5. CIE Illuminants (CIE ILL D$_{65}$ and CIE ILL C). Relative spectral-energy distribution curves

4.6 Standard Illuminants (CIE)

Because the perceived colors of objects generally vary with the illumination in which they are viewed, we tend to prefer to make color comparisons in daylight. But in color specification and color measurement, the wavelength composition of daylight must be specified precisely. For this reason, it has been found practical to establish internationally acceptable standards in the form of arbitrary, yet typical, wavelength compositions.

These standards, called *CIE Illuminants*, have been established by the C.I.E. (Commission Internationale de l'Eclairage). (In the 1930s and 1940s, it was common in the U.S.A. to refer to the Commission by its English name or initials, International Commission on Illumination, I.C.I., but they are no longer used [Ref.4.10, p. 4].) It is to be emphasized that the standard illuminants are, in reality, tables of numbers that state fixed wavelength compositions. Light that has these wavelength compositions may be produced in color-measurement laboratories by use of special lamps and filters. Fig.4.4 and 4.5 show plots that represent several important CIE illuminants.

One illuminant, called CIE Illuminant A, or simply *CIE ILL A*, represents closely the wavelength composition of light from a 500-watt tungsten-filament light bulb (2850 K, Sect.7.10) [Ref.3.7, p. 47]. The relative spectral-energy distribution curve for CIE ILL A is given in Figs.4.1 and 4.4. Another illuminant, *CIE ILL B*, typifies the wavelength composition of direct sunlight. CIE ILL C is particularly important, because its wavelength composition is typical of that of daylight. Most color measurements from the 1930s to the 1960s were reported in terms of CIE ILL C; some useful tools for considering colors relate to this illuminant (Sect.7.1,5; 8.4,5,8).

CIE ILL B and CIE ILL C represent the wavelength composition of sunlight and of daylight rather well, but only in the range from 400 to 700 nm [4.11]. For color measurement of fluorescent materials, illuminants should be used whose relative energies in the wavelength range from 300 to 400 nm also typify those of sunlight and daylight. A new series of standard illuminants was introduced recently that represents well the wavelength compositions of various phases of daylight, the most common being CIE ILL D_{55}, CIE ILL D_{65}, and CIE ILL D_{75} [4.12].

For the most part, CIE ILL C has been replaced by CIE ILL D_{65}, which represents the wavelength composition of typical daylight in the range from 300 to 830 nm [4.11]. The new series is based on a thorough investigation of the wavelength compositions of daylight. In Fig.4.5, the relative spectral-energy distribution curves for CIE ILL C and CIE ILL D_{65} [4.12] can be compared. It is clear that only in the region below 380 nm do the two curves differ significantly.

It is useful to know about the principal standard illuminants, because they are commonly part of technical color specifications. In a color specification, the illuminant describes the illumination of an object for which the stated color applies.

4.7 Eye Brightness Sensitivity

Light is described as visible radiation. In Sect.4.3 it was pointed out that the visible range of radiation extends from 380 to 780 nm. In general, a normal eye is essentially blind to all radiation of wavelengths shorter than 380 nm and longer than 780 nm. How well does the normal eye respond within the range of visibility?

Thorough investigations have been performed to provide the answer. They show that the brightness sensitivity of a normal eye to monochromatic light increases as the wavelength is increased, starting from zero sensation at about 380 nm. The brightness sensitivity reaches a maximum at about 555 nm and then decreases, reaching zero at about 780 nm. The internationally accepted set of data representing an "average" normal eye is presented in part in Table 4.2. These data are referred to as *relative luminosity*; they have their maximum value of 1.000 at 555 nm. A graph of the data is the bell-shaped curve (II) in Fig.6.8, which is used in color-measurement calculations (Sect.6.3).

The bell-shaped curve shows that at wavelengths 510 and 610 nm the relative luminosity is 0.500. This implies that a typical normal eye is half as sensitive to radiation at wavelengths 510 and 610 nm as at 555 nm. The hue response to monochromatic radiation at 555 nm is yellowish green; at 510 nm, green; and at 610 nm, reddish orange. At 472 nm (blue) and at 650 nm (red) the brightness sensitivities of the normal human eye are about one-tenth its brightness sensitivity at 555 nm.

5. Colored Materials

5.1 Pigments and Dyes

Substances used to color materials (pigments and dyes) are called *colorants*. *Dyes* are soluble substances, or substances that are soluble during a stage of a dyeing process. They are commonly used to color textiles, paper, plastics, leather, etc. Certain classes of dyes are rendered insoluble by a chemical process after they have penetrated into the material being dyed. *Pigments* are insoluble substances particles of which are dispersed in paints, lacquers, inks, paper, plastics, rubber, etc. *Fluorescent pigments* for paints are commonly dyes dissolved in a plastic. The dye and plastic ingredients are combined before the plastic is transformed chemically into an insoluble solid and ground to a powder.

Thousands of dyes and pigments are in current use. Of these, a relatively small number are of interest to artists and designers. LEVISON, in his book on the lightfastness of artists' pigments, lists about 100 pigments that are now being used by artists or that are of potential use to them [5.1]. Information about artists' pigments of the present and of the past may be found in handbooks by MAYER [5.2], WEHLTE [5.3], and GETTENS and STOUT [5.4]. A comprehensive listing of virtually all current industrial colorants is provided in the *Colour Index* in six volumes [5.5,6]. In the *Colour Index*, colorants are classified by use, composition, and trade name. Because new colorants are frequently becoming commercially available, the *Colour Index* is kept up-to-date by the publication "Additions and Amendments".

5.2 Opaque Materials

Most objects that we view are opaque. Light that falls on an opaque paint surface (nonfluorescent) is affected by the surface material in three different ways. Part of the incident light is reflected away without entering the surface (*surface reflection*). The wavelength composition of surface-reflected light is nearly unchanged; it is nearly identical to that of the incident light. If the paint surface is *matte*, *diffuse surface reflection* occurs; the bare, rough pigment particles that poke out of the paint surface cause surface reflection in all directions. If the surface is smooth and *glossy*, then surface reflection of incident light is mirrorlike; it is called *specular reflection* [Ref.2.1, p. 36]. Diffuse ambient light that arrives from all directions at a glossy surface is, of course, reflected in all directions.

The rest of the light, usually the major part, penetrates the surface. It passes through pigment particles in which some is *selectively absorbed*; the remainder is scattered back diffusely to the surroundings. The selectively absorbed light is converted to heat; it disappears unnoticed. Selective light absorption by pigments and dyes means that light is absorbed in varying amounts, depending on wavelength. The wavelength dependence of the absorption is determined by certain chemical structures that characterize individual colorants. As a consequence, the wavelength composition of the unabsorbed light that leaves a pigmented or dyed material differs from that of the incident light.

If there were a white pigment of perfect whiteness in the paint, then light that penetrates the pigment particles would not be absorbed. The light would be scattered diffusely from within the paint film and would have the same wavelength composition as the incident light. High-quality white pigments do absorb light selectively, but in only a minor way.

Thus, the three ways by which incident light is affected are surface reflection, selective absorption, and scattering. If daylight (white light) falls on a matte paint film pigmented with cadmium red, the light that reaches our eyes is a mixture of white light (surface-reflected light) and red light (light that remains after selective absorption). The perceived color, also called *object color* or, more specifically, *surface color*, is red. The saturation of the red depends on both the selectivity of the absorption and the amount of dilution of the red light by the surface-reflected light.

Figure 5.1 shows *spectral reflectance curves* for two artists' pigment powders measured by BARNES [5.7,8]. Only a minimum amount of vehicle (glue) was present to hold the pigment particles together to form a matte layer. The *reflectance* of an opaque material is the fraction or percentage of the incident light that the material does not absorb [Ref.2.2, p. 187]. If the reflectance is measured at 5 or 10 nm intervals over the whole visible range (380-780 nm), the results can be plotted as a spectral reflectance curve.

Curve I for cadmium red shows that the pigment exposed to white light absorbs less than half of the light that it receives in the wavelength range above 600 nm and absorbs most of the light at wavelengths below 600 nm. Mad-

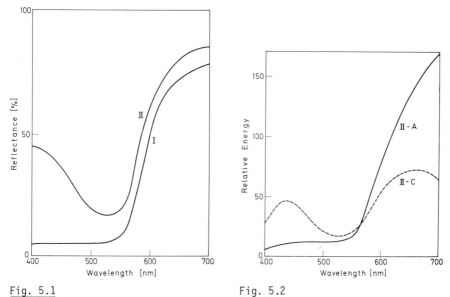

Fig. 5.1   Fig. 5.2

Fig. 5.1. Cadmium red (I) and madder lake (II) pigments. Spectral reflectance curves for matte paint films. (Based on curves published in [5.7,8])

Fig. 5.2. Madder lake pigment. Wavelength composition of light reflected from a matte paint film (madder lake pigment [5.7,8]) when illuminated by daylight (II-C), typified by CIE ILL C, and by incandescent lamp light (II-A), typified by CIE ILL A. Relative spectral-energy distribution curves

der lake (II), however, absorbs relatively small proportions of the light at wavelengths both above 600 nm (red) and below 480 nm (blue). The result is that, when madder lake is illuminated by daylight, magenta light (a mixture of essentially red and blue light) passes from the pigment particles to the eye.

Spectral reflectance curves I and II in Fig.5.1 represent the simultaneous occurrence of surface reflection and selective absorption. Thus, the red light that comes from the interior of the pigment particles is diluted by mixture with some surface-reflected white light (typified by CIE ILL C). The spectral reflectance curve in the case of the cadmium red pigment shows that below 550 nm about 5% of the incident light was not absorbed. It is possible that surface-reflected white light accounted for most, or even all, of the 5%.

Glossy paint films and varnished oil paintings often have colors of greater saturation than those of matte films that contain the same pigment. The reason is that, in the former, the pigment particles at the paint-film surface are covered by a smooth glossy layer of paint vehicle (for example, dried linseed oil) or of varnish resin. In a red glossy paint film, for example, some of the red light is reflected from the smooth surface back into the pigment particles again (*internal reflection*) where it is subjected to further absorption. This red light, which results from two passages of the light through the film, is combined with the red light that is not internally reflected and with surface-reflected white light to produce a mixture of light whose color is more saturated than the color obtainable with the same pigment in a matte film [Ref.2.2, p. 283].

The saturation of the color can be increased by viewing the glossy film when it is illuminated by a direct beam of light such as a sunbeam. Even better results can be obtained by illumination with a projector beam in a darkened room, to avoid illumination with diffuse ambient light, which could produce diffuse, desaturating reflection in all directions. With isolated direct lighting, the white light that is specularly reflected from the surface, as from a mirror, can easily be avoided by a viewer, so that only undiluted red light reaches the eye [Ref.2.2, p. 282].

The spectral reflectance curves in Fig.5.1 do not show the wavelength composition of the light that comes from illuminated cadmium red and madder lake pigments. The wavelength composition of the light that leaves a paint film depends not only on the absorption characteristics of the pigments and on the surface reflection but also on the wavelength composition of the incident light. The effect of the incident light is illustrated in Fig.5.2. One curve (II-C) represents the relative spectral distribution curve for the light coming from the madder lake film when it is exposed to daylight (typified by CIE ILL C). Curve II-A is for light that comes from a film that contains the same pigment when it is illuminated by an incandescent tungsten-filament lamp (typified by CIE ILL A). The wavelength compositions of CIE ILL C and CIE ILL A are shown in Fig.4.4. Because light from incandescent lamps is richer in radiant energy at longer wavelengths (the reds) and leaner in radiant energy at shorter wavelengths (the blues) (such light is often said to be "warm"), the light scattered by the pigment tends to be richer in longer wavelengths and leaner in shorter wavelengths. Thus, in incandescent-lamp illumination, the madder lake pigment appears red, not magenta, because, as curve II-A shows, the blue content of the reflected light is very low.

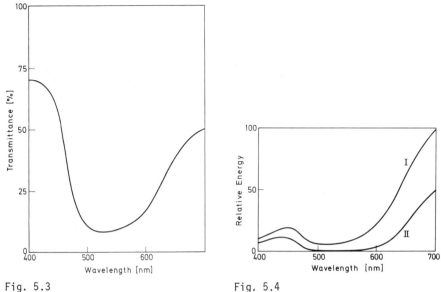

Fig. 5.3

Fig. 5.4

Fig. 5.3. Red-purple glass. 1 mm thickness. Spectral transmittance curve

Fig. 5.4. Red-purple glass. Wavelength composition of light after it passes through glass of 1 mm thickness (I) and 2 mm (II) when illuminated by an incandescent lamp whose light is typified by CIE ILL A. Relative spectral-energy distribution curves

5.3 Transparent Materials

The phenomena that occur when light falls on a *transparent* material, such as colored glass or plastic, are essentially no different from those that occur when light falls on an opaque paint film. Part of the light that passes through the transparent material (nonfluorescent) is absorbed and dissipated, unnoticed, as heat; the remainder that is not absorbed emerges from the opposite side as *transmitted light*. (I am not now taking into account the simultaneous occurrence of internal reflection.) When daylight enters one side of a colored glass, and red light is transmitted from the other side to our eyes, we say that the glass is red — that is, the perceived color (object color) is red.

There is one difference to be noted, however. If an opaque matte red paint film is viewed in daylight, the red light that reaches the eyes from within the pigment particles is diluted by white light (daylight) that is reflected diffusely from the surface of the film. In the case of a transparent red glass, for example, there is also surface reflection of diffuse white light, but this white light does not mix with the transmitted red light, because it reflects from the glass in the opposite direction — that is, away from the eyes.

A *spectral transmittance curve* for a red-purple glass of 1 mm thickness is shown in Fig.5.3. The *transmittance* of a transparent material is the fraction or percentage of the incident light that passes completely through the material. A spectral transmittance curve is analogous to a spectral reflectance curve for an opaque material. The red-purple glass allows red light (wavelengths longer than 630 nm) and blue light (wavelengths shorter than 480 nm) to pass through it; like the pigment madder lake, it absorbs most of the light of intermediate wavelengths.

Figure 5.4 shows the relative spectral-energy distribution curve I for the light that emerges from the red-purple glass of 1 mm thickness when it is illuminated by an incandescent tungsten-filament lamp (typified by CIE ILL A). Because the relative amount of blue light (radiant energy at lower wavelengths) in the lamp light is low (Fig.4.1), only a small amount of blue light is transmitted, as the small hump at the left end of curve I indicates. The color of this light is pink (chromaticity: 0.440, 0.279) (Fig.7.1). [When daylight (CIE ILL C) passes through the glass, the color is purple (chromaticity: 0.261, 0.144).] Curve II shows the relative spectral energy distribution of the light that is transmitted in the case of two layers of glass or of one layer of 2 mm thickness. It is significant that the curves (Fig.5.4) move to lower positions when the number of layers or the layer thickness increases: the brightness of the transmitted light diminishes. It is also significant that the "valleys" decrease to lower positions faster than the "summits" (of the humps): the saturation increases and the hue may change.

Now we might ask what occurs in the case of a transparent colored paint film on white paper. Let us consider the case of a paint film that has the characteristics shown in Fig.5.3. If light from an incandescent tungsten-filament lamp falls on the paint film, curve I in Fig.5.4 could represent the wavelength composition of the pink light that reaches the surface of the paper after traversing the film. If we can assume that the white paper reflects all of the light that reaches it and that the reflection is diffuse, then the light would pass through the paint film again, but in the opposite direction, and would emerge as red-purple light (chromaticity: 0.383, 0.168) having the wavelength composition given by curve II (Fig.5.4) on reaching the film surface. Of course, if the red-purple light that emerges from the film surface were diluted by diffuse surface-reflected light (about 4% of the incident light), then, instead of curve II, another curve that includes the contribution of surface-reflected light would represent the total reflected light.

5.4 Fluorescent Materials

Paints, inks, and plastics that contain fluorescent dyes are used commonly in advertising and decoration. Artist Richard BOWMAN began using fluorescent lacquers in his paintings in 1950 [5.9]; the use of fluorescent paints and inks in art has been spreading widely. Many of the colors produced by fluorescent dyes viewed in, say, sunlight cannot be produced by nonfluorescent dyes and pigments under the same conditions (Sect.7.6).

In what way do the phenomena that occur in nonfluorescent and fluorescent materials differ when they are illuminated by daylight or lamp light? For our purposes here it is helpful to recall that, after light penetrates into an opaque or transparent nonfluorescent material, part of the received light is absorbed selectively and the remainder is scattered back or transmitted. The absorbed light is transformed to heat, which disappears unnoticed. It should be added that ultraviolet radiation that passes into a nonfluorescent material undergoes the same changes: part is absorbed selectively and transformed completely to heat, and the remainder is scattered back or transmitted as ultraviolet radiation.

When visible radiant energy (light) and ultraviolet radiation penetrate into a *fluorescent material*, again some is scattered back or transmitted and the remainder is absorbed. What is different in the case of fluorescent materials is that *only part* (*not all*) of the absorbed light and ultraviolet radiation is transformed to heat. The remaining absorbed part is transformed and *reemitted as radiant energy at longer wavelengths* [5.10]. When this transformed energy is reemitted as visible radiation (light), it *adds* to the light normally scattered or transmitted from the material. The result is that the light that leaves the surface is increased to such a level, within certain wavelength regions, in relation to the surrounds, that often what is known as a fluorescent appearance is perceived. It should be emphasized that fluorescence can occur in some materials without evoking the visual perception of fluorescence [3.4].

Examples of fluorescent materials can be found in which only ultraviolet radiation is transformed to longer-wave visible radiant energy. But the materials of perhaps greater practical interest are those in which both ultra-

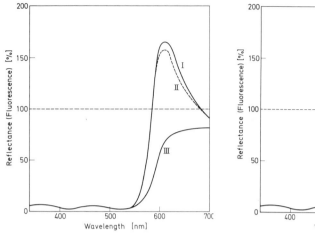
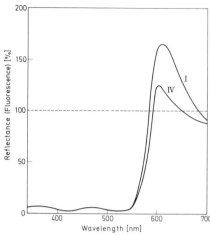

Fig. 5.5   Fig. 5.6

Fig. 5.5. Fluorescent red film on white paper. Spectral reflectance curves
for illumination by sunlight (I), by sunlight with the ultraviolet portion
filtered out (II), and by sunlight with all radiation below 580 nm filtered
out (III). From [Ref.5.12, Fig.7](copyright of the Institute of Physics)

Fig. 5.6. Fluorescent red film on white paper. Spectral reflectance curves
for illumination by sunlight (I) (from Fig.5.5) and by light from an incandescent lamp (IV) (estimated on the basis of [Ref.5.13, Fig.9])

violet radiation and short-wave visible radiant energy are transformed and
produce what is called *daylight fluorescence* [5.11].

An example of what may occur is indicated by the curves in Fig.5.5 for a
transparent fluorescent red film on paper exposed to sunlight [5.12]. Curve I
shows the reflectance augmented by fluorescence contributions. At wavelengths
shorter than 550 nm most of the light was absorbed. Within the wavelength
range 580-680 nm, the curve arches to 165%, well above the horizontal dashed
line that represents the spectral reflectance curve of an ideal white surface. It is clear that *within an appreciable wavelength range* more light was
being emitted than was being received. The explanation is that part of the
large amount of radiant energy (ultraviolet radiation and light) that was
absorbed at wavelengths shorter than 580 nm was transformed and reemitted as
light of longer wavelengths, from about 580 nm to over 700 nm.

Curve II (dashed) is interesting because it shows results obtained when
sunlight was filtered to eliminate all ultraviolet radiation (wavelengths
shorter than 380 nm) before falling on the red film. The area between curves
I and II represents the contribution (only about 10%) made by the sun's ul-

traviolet radiation. Curve III indicates the portion that is not absorbed when the light received on the film is sunlight from which both ultraviolet radiation and light at wavelengths shorter than 580 nm have been filtered out to prevent fluorescence. Over the wavelength range 580-700 nm, curve III is an ordinary spectral reflectance curve for the red film treated like a nonfluorescent material. The area between curves II and III is great. It indicates the significant contribution to the visible emissions by wavelengths longer than 580 nm, caused by transformation of radiant energy absorbed in the visible range between 380 and 580 nm. Knowing this we should not be surprised to find that the red film appears red when it is illuminated with blue light [5.12].

Spectral reflectance and spectral transmittance curves for nonfluorescent materials do not depend upon the light sources used for illumination. They apply equally well to light of different wavelength compositions. The curves for fluorescent materials do depend upon the wavelength composition of the illumination. Hence, curve I in Fig.5.5 takes into account the wavelength composition of sunlight. In Fig.5.6, curve I (from Fig.5.5) may be compared with curve IV for the case with light from an incandescent tungsten-filament lamp [Ref.5.13, p. 36]. The lower peak is explained by the fact that less light is available at wavelengths shorter than 580 nm in a beam from the lamp (typified by CIE ILL A, Fig.4.4), than from sunlight (typified by CIE ILL B, Fig.4.4).

Optical bleaches (or fluorescent brighteners) are used in paper and textile treatment. Such agents absorb ultraviolet radiation and reemit part of it at short wavelengths in the visible range (violet, blue). The result is that yellowness in a fabric, for example, is "neutralized" (the blue emission adds to the emission of yellow, the complementary color, to produce white by additive color mixture, Sect.5.6), and the whiteness is enhanced by the increased amount of light that leaves the surface [5.12].

Some fluorescent pigments appear white or whitish in sunlight, but when viewed in darkness in the presence of "black light" (ultraviolet radiation, Sect.4.1), they glow in highly saturated colors. Minerals that contain fluorescent constituents are often seen displayed in this manner in science museums. Their rich colors often cannot be seen in daylight, because their brightness is much too low in comparison with the brightness of the ambient illumination.

5.5 Metamerism and Matching Colors

Matching of colors involves a phenomenon that is fundamental to an understanding of the purpose and method of CIE color specification. It should be considered here, at least briefly. To introduce the idea, let us consider the following example. A small area of green paint has been scraped from a uniformly painted and uniformly illuminated wall. Now it is necessary to repaint the scraped area. House painters and willing artists are able to produce an excellent match even when the pigments in the paint they use are different from the pigments present in the surrounding old paint. But how can the match be a good one? Are not the spectral reflectance curves for the new and old paint films different? Yes, in answer to the second question, the spectral reflectance curves for the two paint films may be very different.

The answer to the first question is related to the fact that the eye cannot identify the wavelength composition (spectral energy distribution) of light [Ref.2.4, p. 25]. (In a way, the ear is more analytical than the eye, because it can detect the musical tones in a chord.) In fact, *one* color response, for example a particular green, can be evoked by any one of a set of stimuli that have different wavelength compositions (relative energy distribution curves). This set of stimuli is called a *metameric set*. The stimuli in such a set are called *metamers*, and the matching property of such stimuli is called *metamerism*. In the case of matching paint, the *stimuli* (the light that comes to the eye from the two paint films) are matched. (The matched stimuli are metamers.) In reality, paints containing different pigments are not matched by the eye; only the stimuli are.

In addition, we should recall that the wavelength composition of the light that enters the eye depends not only on the spectral reflectance curves of the two green paint films but also on the wavelength composition of the light that falls on the paint films (Sect.5.2, Fig.5.2). If the wavelength composition of the illumination that falls on the "matching" paint films is changed (for example, from that of light from an incandescent lamp to that of light from a fluorescent lamp), then it is almost certain that stimuli that come from the two films will no longer be metamers and that the perceived colors will be different; the "match" will no longer be good.

The number of stimuli in a metameric set can vary widely. In the case of white light, the number of metamers in the set is very large (Sect.7.4). This means that light of a very large number of different wavelength compositions can produce the white response. The number in a set is much smaller when the colors of the spectrum are approached. For each of the colors of the spectrum there is but one stimulus, monochromatic light; the wavelength composition is given by one wavelength, for example 590 nm for a certain orange light. D.B. JUDD estimated that there are more than 10 million metamer sets — that is, more than 10 million colors — that can be discriminated by an unaided normal eye under suitable viewing conditions [Ref.2.4, p. 29].

Light sources can be devised whose beams are metameric (metameric illumination [Ref.2.4, p. 217]). Startling demonstrations can be made with them. For example, a beam can be produced that is metameric with daylight, such that a sheet of paper (white in daylight) is also white in the beam, but a lemon (yellow in daylight) is red in the same beam (Sect.7.4).

5.6 Additive Color Mixture

Just as the term "matching paint" is inaccurate, because in reality the stimulus light, not paint, is matched, so the term "color mixture" is inaccurate, because it is a stimulus light, not a response color, that is mixed. There would be some merit in replacing "color mixture" by a scientifically more correct term like "color-stimulus synthesis" [Ref.2.1, p. 115], just as there would be in replacing the usual commercial term "ice cream" by a term closer to the mark like "frozen milk product". But I am sure that it is more important both to be aware of the facts and to maintain general communication by using universally adopted terms. With this in mind, let us proceed to the subjects of additive color mixture, subtractive color mixture, and color mixture by averaging.

Additive color mixture occurs when light from two or more sources is combined (added together) before it reaches the eye. A helpful way to demonstrate the effect is to project two beams of colored light onto a white wall, so that the two disks of light are superimposed and the combined light from the two beams is scattered from the wall. Because the two beams are added together, the energy in the combination is equal to the sum of the two initial beams. The effect is apparent in the resulting enhanced brightness when one disk is superimposed on the other [Ref.2.4, p. 74]. If the perceived hues of the two initial beams are different, the resulting combined beam will generally be perceived to have an intermediate hue. Thus, if the beams are red and green, the hue of the superimposed disks may be yellow-green, yellow, or orange, depending on the relative intensities of the initial beams. If, however, the hues are sufficiently different (on opposite sides of the color circle discussed in Sect.5.10), for example a red and a blue-green, then it is possible with appropriate relative light intensities to produce white light. In this case, the two original colors are called *complementary colors*. In general, the saturation of the color of the combined beam is less than that of at least one of the original beams. With complementary colors, of course, the saturation of the color of the combined beam can be as low as zero (white light).

5.7 Subtractive Color Mixture

As described, additive color mixture can be demonstrated by the combination of two or more beams of light of different color to produce a beam of greater intensity and of a different color. Subtractive color mixture, on the other hand, can be demonstrated by one beam, from which energy in different amounts at various wavelengths is removed (subtracted) by two or more successive absorptions.

The subtracting process can be demonstrated by passing a beam of sunlight successively through two pieces of colored glass (light filters), one yellow and the other green, to produce light of color yellow-green. When sunlight falls on the yellow glass, the yellow light transmitted has a wavelength composition that shows that most of the shorter-wavelength light (blue to green) is absorbed in the glass and that much of the yellow-green and most of the yellow, orange, and red light is transmitted. On the other hand, the green light produced when sunlight is passed through the green glass has a wavelength composition that shows that relatively large amounts of blue-green, green, and yellow-green light are transmitted and that most of the blue, yellow, orange, and red light is absorbed. From this, it is clear that when the beam of light is passed through one glass and then through the other, only the yellow-green light emerges, because practically all of the other light is absorbed (subtracted out). Thus subtractive color mixture occurs when filters are "mixed" (placed in tandem) through which light passes successively.

The same process occurs, although probably not exclusively, when paints are mixed, for example yellow and green oil paints. A ray of daylight that enters the paint film passes through a mixture of yellow and green pigment particles, eventually emerging as yellow-green light. Subtractive color mixture can also be demonstrated by passing a beam of light through a solution of two dyes. Again, each colorant (yellow or green dye) selectively absorbs light in its own way and the emerging beam is composed of wavelengths that largely escape both absorption processes (yellow-green). Because energy is removed from the beam by the absorption, the brightness of the emerging beam in subtractive color mixture is always diminished.

5.8 Color Mixture by Averaging

Additive color mixture is the name for the process of combining light beams of different colors before they reach the eye. Beams can, in effect, be combined in the visual process as when light beams of different color stimulate the same portion of the retina but without superposition [Ref.2.1, p. 115]. This can occur when an array of tiny beams of different colors is more minute in detail than is the "weave" or "mosaic" of receptor cells and interconnected nerve cells that receive the array. In such a case, the different colors are not resolved and a kind of retinal area mixture or blending takes place, which is sometimes called spatial averaging [Ref.2.1, p. 115]. A combination can also occur in the visual process when a rapid succession of flashes of light of alternating colors falls on an area of the retina. If the change is too rapid for the visual process to keep pace, retinal temporal mixture, or temporal averaging, results [Ref.2.1, p. 115; Ref.2.3, p. 66]. In both cases, there is a "mixed" response: the mixed color is seen. These two kinds of combination (area and temporal mixture) are called *color mixture by averaging*. Thus, a printed paragraph of words in black letters on white paper becomes a gray area when viewed from a sufficient distance; the gray is the result of color mixture (black and white) by averaging (area mixture). The same occurs when juxtaposed dots of three different colors are viewed on a television screen, or in halftone printing on paper. The same may occur when a pointillistic painting is viewed at sufficient distance so that the dabs of paint of different color are not individually distinguished. When the painting is approached more closely and the individual color dabs begin to become distinguishable, other effects occur [Ref.2.4, p. 214; 2.6]. Another example of rapidly alternating stimuli leading to color mixture by averaging (temporal mixture) is a rapidly turning disk on whose surface sectors have different colors. A disk whose surface is covered by black and white sectors appears gray.

The difference between additive color mixture and color mixture by averaging is implied by the two terms. In additive color mixture, the energy of two combined beams is the result of adding the energy of the two initial beams, and the brightness is increased. In color mixture by averaging, the effective energies of the stimuli are area-averaged or time-averaged in the visual process, and a kind of average brightness is produced.

5.9 The Primaries

To many, the terms *primaries* and *primary colors* suggest bright red, yellow, and blue paints. With such paints, with white and black in addition, mixtures can be made of a wide range of hues, lightness, and saturation. But, if we wish to consider color mixture and matching in a broader sense, further elucidation of the notion of the primaries as stimuli is essential.

A characteristic of a set of three primaries is that no combination of any two of them matches the third [Ref.2.1, p. 119]. To have particular utility, the qualification is usually added that the three primaries be selected so that the gamut of colors obtainable by mixing them includes all hues and is as large as is practical.

A very large gamut of colors that includes all hues may be produced by mixtures (additive color mixture) of varying proportions of monochromatic light of three wavelengths: 700 nm (red), 535 nm (yellowish green), and 400 nm (bluish purple, or violet) [Ref.2.2, p. 238]. The color gamut includes all of the purples and most of the reds, oranges, and yellows, but the highly saturated greens and blues are excluded (Sect.7.3). Three such stimuli are called *additive primaries*. In a less specific way, the additive primaries are ordinarily said to be stimuli that produce the responses *red*, *green*, and *blue*.

In situations where subtractive color mixture is used, the *subtractive primaries* are of some importance. The colors produced by each of the three subtractive primaries are complementary to red, green, and blue — namely,

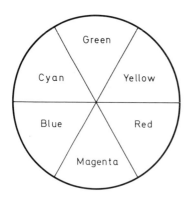

Fig. 5.7. Goethe color circle

cyan (blue-green or turquoise), *magenta* (purplish red), and *yellow*, respectively. Cyan, magenta, and yellow pigments and dyes are used in color photography and in the four-color (including black, to improve blackness and definition) printing process. In these cases, there is an advantage in having to deal with only three or four dyes or inks. But, admittedly, painters and designers, who use tubes or jars of paint of a great variety of colors, may not find the subject of subtractive primaries directly relevant to their work. On the other hand, as will be shown in the following chapters, the additive primaries are basically relevant in art and design involving color.

5.10 Color Circles

Color circles of the type familiar to artists generally present printed color samples in the hue sequence found in a rainbow. The color circle is completed by inserting the nonspectral colors (purples and purplish reds) between red and violet. Colors can be selected to form a color circle such that pairs of complementary colors are directly opposite each other [Ref.2.1, p. 116].

A circle of six members may be formed that has samples which represent the three additive primary colors and their complementary colors, the subtractive primary colors. Intermediate complementary-color pairs may be introduced, to increase the number of colors to 12, 24, 48, 96, or 192. In a color circle that contains 192 colors, the difference between the hues of adjacent colors is hardly perceptible (Sect.3.2).

The six-member color circle is properly called the *Goethe color circle*, for Goethe is credited for describing it [Ref.5.3, p. 664] (Sect.1.1). An example of such a circle is shown in Fig.5.7 and Plate I. The opposing colors in Plate I were chosen to be complementary (Sect.7.2). GERRITSEN, who objects to the old practice of teaching that the primary colors are blue, red, and yellow, has proposed a color circle of this type as a teaching aid [5.15].

6. Color Specification (CIE)

6.1 Light and Color: Other Definitions

The subject of color measurement, *colorimetry*, is in the domain called psychophysics, which lies between the domains of psychology, physics, physiology, and chemistry [Ref.4.10, p. 40]. In the early 1930s, colorimetry was put on a universally accepted precise quantitative basis. The new practical scheme, however, required a redefinition of basic terms.

As stated in Sect.4.1, in physics, light is defined as visible radiant energy. In psychophysics, a distinction is made between light and visible radiant energy. Here the meaning of the term "visible radiant energy" is retained in the physical sense: the stimulus of vision [Ref.4.10, p. 40] — that is, radiant energy in the range from 380 to 780 nm. Sometimes visible radiant energy is termed "light stimulus" [Ref.2.3, p. 377].

Light, on the other hand, has been defined in psychophysics to take account of a human observer's awareness: light is "the aspect of radiant energy of which the human observer is aware through the agency of his eyes and the associated nervous system" [Ref.4.10, p. 40]. The distinction is clear if we consider that we are not equally aware of visible radiation received in equal amounts at 381 nm (barely visible) and 555 nm (of maximum visibility). Thus, in psychophysics "visible radiant energy" refers to all radiation in the visible range, and "light" signifies that radiation in proportion to its effectiveness in producing vision.

With light thus considered in the psychophysical sense, we can proceed to the psychophysical definition of "color". In psychophysics the psychological aspect, perceived color, is referred to by the use of the term "sensation of color". But the word "color" in psychophysics denotes a characteristic of the *stimulus* — that is, of the visible radiant energy that produces the sensation of color [Ref.2.3, p. 376]. (This is closer to the layman's concept that light is colored.) It takes into account both the radiant energy that reaches the eye and a standard observer who has typical normal color vision and, hence, makes typical use of the radiation that produces vision. The Committee on Colorimetry of the Optical Society of America, having accepted the psychophysical concept, after much study, concluded, "This course seems to be amply justified on purely philosophical grounds, but, if less academic justification is desired, the purely practical considerations are fully sufficient" [Ref.4.10, p. 40].

Colors can be measured by finding a match to one of a series of standard samples (such as printed papers, dyed fabrics, and paint swatches or chips) under standardized conditions of viewing. For greater accuracy, devices called colorimeters can be used. In one type of colorimeter, the field of view contains the color sample and the comparison color. The latter is varied by three kinds of adjustments until a match is found. The color is then expressed in terms of three numbers that, in the case of some instruments, are the internationally accepted *CIE tristimulus values* (Sect.6.2) or are convertible to them. Photoelectric colorimeters operate automatically; in them the human eye is replaced by a photoelectric cell.

A colorimeter provides a direct measurement of color. There is an indirect method, however, that is more precise and rather extensively employed. The method involves use of a spectrophotometer to obtain a spectral reflectance curve for an opaque sample (Sect.5.2) or a spectral transmittance curve for a transparent sample (Sect.5.3). With the use of either curve, the CIE tristimulus values can be calculated in a routine manner for the sample in a selected kind of illumination (for example, illumination typified by CIE ILL C or CIE ILL D_{65}). The possibility of human error in making direkt color measurements is avoided in this procedure. This indirect approach is of particular interest, because the scheme established for it provides access to the structure that underlies the CIE tristimulus values, which are basic to precise specification of colors.

6.2 The Chromaticity Diagram: An Introduction

In this section and in the following one, the structure underlying the CIE tristimulus values is discussed in a general way. The structure is founded on well-established principles of additive color mixture known as Grassmann's laws. (Discussions of these laws may be found in standard texts on colorimetry, such as [2.1,3;3.7;6.1].)

To begin, it is helpful to consider the example of three beams of short, medium, and long wavelengths used as a set of three additive primaries (red, green, and blue). Different colors are produced by superimposing the disks of the three beams (additive color mixture) on a white wall and varying the

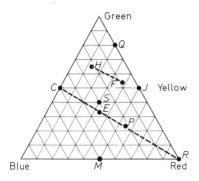

Fig. 6.1. Chromaticity diagram or Maxwell triangle (equal-sided triangle)

amount (intensity) of light in each beam. If the color produced by a fourth beam of light is within the gamut of colors that can be produced by mixtures of the three beams, then the color can be specified by the amounts of each of the three beams required to match it.

A set of three additive primary colors and the complete gamut of colors obtainable by mixing two and three of them can be represented on a kind of *mixture diagram*, an equal-sided (equilateral) triangle, the so-called *Maxwell triangle*, named after the Scottish physicist James Clerk Maxwell (1831-1879), who employed it in his basic work on color. The three primaries are assigned to points at the corners of the triangle. The gamut of colors of all possible mixtures of the particular primaries is represented by points on the three sides of the triangle and by points within it (Fig.6.1).

The representation of psychophysical color by the triangle is partial. The part that is represented is called the *chromaticity*, and, indeed, it is now much more common to refer to the triangle as a *chromaticity diagram*. Chromaticity is the quality aspect of psychophysical color; it is a composite representation of approximate equivalents of psychological hue and saturation. The part not included on the diagram, the quantity aspect of psychophysical color, is the effective amount of light — that is, the amount of psychophysical light defined in the previous section. It is the amount sensed in the visual process. Because the eye's efficiency in responding to a given amount of radiation varies from zero at the limits of visibility (380 and 780 nm) to a maximum at 555 nm (Sect.4.7), the psychophysical amount is taken as the physical amount weighted by the eye's efficiency.

A condition imposed on the selection of the colors to serve as primaries is that, when the beams are combined in psychophysically equal amounts, the color white is produced on a white screen or wall. The chromaticity of equal-

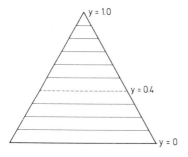

Fig. 6.2. Lines of constant y (see Fig.6.1)

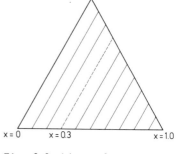

Fig. 6.3. Lines of constant x (see Fig.6.1)

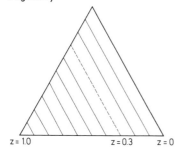

Fig. 6.4. Lines of constant z (see Fig.6.1)

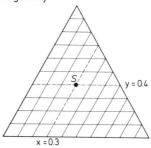

Fig. 6.5. Location of point S

energy white is represented by point E at the center of the chromaticity diagram (Sect.6.3).

Although the equal-sided triangular chromaticity diagram is employed rarely, it is instructive to consider it a bit further before we discuss the diagram that is in present-day use. It may be presented on triangular-coordinate paper, which is subdivided by three superimposed sets of parallel lines. The three sets are shown separately in relation to the triangle in Figs.6.2, 6.3, and 6.4.

It is helpful to borrow the CIE symbols X, Y, and Z; these represent the CIE tristimulus values, which are defined for the particular set of primaries discussed in Sect.6.3. Here, however, they are taken to represent the amounts of the three primaries now being discussed (X, amount of red; Y, amount of green; and Z, amount of blue) needed in a mixture to match a color within the gamut. The relative proportions or *fractional amounts* (given by x, red; y, green; and z, blue) clearly represent the quality aspect of psychophysical color and, we shall see, they locate the chromaticity by a point on the chromaticity diagram.

If the tristimulus values are X = 60, Y = 80, and Z = 60, then the fractional amount of primary red x, for example, is the amount of red 60 divided by the total amount 200, which is 0.3. The calculations similarly yield 0.4 for y and 0.3 for z. The chromaticity of the color can now be represented on the diagram.

Figure 6.2 shows a series of parallel lines along each of which y does not vary, for values of y from zero at the base of the triangle (0% primary green in the mixture) to 1.0 at the vertex of the triangle (100% primary green). Because y = 0.4, the sought point must be located somewhere on the line labeled y = 0.4, shown as a dashed line. Fig.6.3 presents similar information for the primary red. Because x = 0.3, the point must be located on the line labeled x = 0.3. The point can be located on both lines simultaneously only at their intersection (Fig.6.5). By use of Fig.6.5, the sought point S can be transferred to the chromaticity diagram (Fig.6.1). It is clear that the information z = 0.3 and the point's location on a line labeled z = 0.3 in Fig.6.4 are not needed. *Only two* fractional amounts (for example, x and y) are necessary to locate the point and to specify the chromaticity. When values are given for x and y, the value for z can always be obtained by subtracting from 1.0 the sum of the values of x and y.

The chromaticity of the color just discussed is written as (x=0.3, y=0.4) or, more commonly, as (0.3, 0.4). In the case of white (equal-energy white), for which the amounts of the primaries required are equal, the fractional amounts x, y, and z are obviously each equal to 1/3, or 0.333, and the chromaticity is specified by (0.333, 0.333). The central location of point E can be checked by plotting the point by use of the procedure described.

Point Q that is plotted on one side of the diagram shows the chromaticity of a mixture of two primaries, red and green. For a mixture of equal amounts of primaries red and green (X and Y are equal, and Z is zero, no primary blue), both fractional amounts x and y are equal — that is, 1/2, or 0.5 —

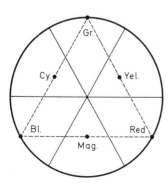

Fig. 6.6. Superposition of the Maxwell triangle and the Goethe color circle (from Fig.5.7)

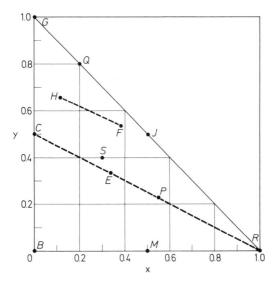

<u>Fig. 6.7.</u> Chromaticity diagram or Maxwell triangle (right triangle)

and the chromaticity is (0.5, 0.5). This chromaticity is represented by point J on the diagram and corresponds to yellow. Similarly, equal amounts of primary red and primary blue result in a light beam that produces the color magenta (0.5, 0.0) (point M); and equal amounts of primary blue and primary green result in the color cyan (0.0, 0.5) (point C). The sequence of the colors around the triangle is the same as that in the Goethe color circle (Fig.6.6).

Complementary colors are found by drawing straight lines across the diagram, through point E, such as the dashed line that connects red and cyan (Fig.6.1). Constructing a line from point Q (yellow-green) through point E to the opposite side would show that the complementary color is a purple. More will be said about the complementary colors in Sect.7.2.

The colors produced by mixture of light are of maximum saturation obtainable by use of the primaries when the chromaticities of the mixtures are located on the sides of the diagram. At the center of the diagram E, the saturation is the minimum, zero. The variation of saturation may be noted by combining a red and a cyan beam. The dashed line in Fig.6.1 is followed, starting from the corner (red) when the red beam is at full intensity and the cyan beam is shut off. Then the intensity of the red beam is diminished progressively and that of the cyan is increased. The saturation of the red decreases continuously through point P (pink). After the saturation reaches

zero at E (white), the hue changes to cyan and the saturation of the colors
increases to a maximum at C. The dashed line that connects red and C is a
mixture line; it represents the gamut of chromaticities possible by mixing
the two beams. Another mixture line is shown between points H and F.

The equal-sided chromaticity diagram, with its triangular grid, is useful
as an introduction to the subject, but it is rather awkward to employ in
practice. It is much more convenient to use a right triangle that has two
equal legs and an ordinary square grid (Fig.6.7). Such a triangle can be used
because it is not necessary to accommodate z on it. All of the points that
appear in Fig.6.1 are also shown in Fig.6.7. The two mixture lines have been
transferred as well. As will be indicated later (Sect.7.3), it is important
that the mixture lines (additive color mixture) are straight.

6.3 The CIE Chromaticity Diagram

It was stated in the previous section that if the color of a beam of light
is within the gamut of colors that can be produced by mixtures of three beams
of primary colors, then the color can be specified by the amounts of each of
the beams required to match it. But what can be done if the color of the beam
is not within the gamut? It is well established that no three primaries can,
by their mixture, produce all colors. This problem can be solved by adding
one of the primary beams to the beam whose color is being measured, to bring
it within the gamut. In such a case, the amount of the primary added is reported as a negative number.

From 1928 to 1930, separate laboratory investigations by W.D. WRIGHT and
by J. GUILD obtained data on the amounts (positive and negative) of three
monochromatic primaries (435.8, 546,1, and 700 nm) needed to match the colors
of the spectrum [Ref.2.1, p. 129; Ref.6.1, p. 99]. Their data, along with the
previously obtained brightness-sensitivity data (Sect.4.7), were adopted by
the CIE to characterize the visual response of a typical normal viewer called
the *CIE standard observer*. The data serve as the basis of the internationally
accepted CIE method for color specification.

Although it is possible to deal with negative numbers in colorimetry, for
various practical reasons it was decided by the CIE to produce a scheme in
which negative amounts of primaries do not arise [Ref.6.1, p. 101]. Because
this is not possible with real primaries, it was necessary to invent primaries
that can: the CIE imaginary primaries. These imaginary primaries are relevant
to typical color vision because they are related by means of mathematical

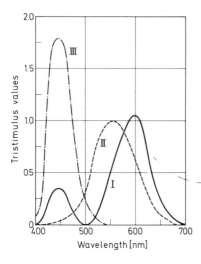

Fig. 6.8. CIE imaginary additive primaries. CIE (1931) color-matching functions: red(I), green(II), and blue(III)

transformations to the laboratory data. Although the gamut of colors produced by mixture of the imaginary primaries includes imaginary colors, these are segregated and ignored; *all real colors* are included in the gamut.

The amounts of the three imaginary primaries necessary to match unit energy of each wavelength in the visible spectrum are recorded as columns of numbers in a table; the three sets of data are called the *color-matching functions* (Fig.6.8): imaginary red (I), imaginary green (II), and imaginary blue (III). From the curves can be read the relative amounts of the imaginary primaries required in additive color mixture to match the colors of monochromatic light (spectrum colors) at any wavelength within the range from 400 to 700 nm. The curves were devised so that when equal amounts of the three primaries are combined they match the equal-energy white (E) (Figs.4.3 and 4.4). The color-matching functions are used in calculations to provide the CIE tristimulus values, which represent the relative amounts of the imaginary primaries required to match a color by additive color mixture [6.2].

An important characteristic of the imaginary primaries red and blue is that they have zero luminance [Ref.6.1, p. 104]. This is a simplification provided by the mathematics that underlies the CIE system. All of the luminance is assigned to the imaginary green primary. The imaginary red and blue primaries were designed so that the color-matching function for imaginary green would be identical to the relative luminosity curve for normal eye brightness sensitivity (Sect.4.7). To understand the significance of this invention, note that, although the imaginary primaries are measured in the same unit (from the fact that the amounts required to produce white by a mixture of the three beams are equal), we do not know what the units are. As a result, the calculated tristimulus values (for example, X=1300, Y=1000, and Z=1100) have only relative meaning. But because Y is given an alternate meaning, luminance, a separate measurement is made that provides an *absolute* number, not a relative one, for example Y = 200 (luminance units). Then, to specify the color, the tristimulus values can be adjusted in proportion to give Y = 200, thus: X = 260, Y = 200, and Z = 220. However, it is conventional, in the case of lights, to report the tristimulus values on the basis of Y = 100 (hence, X=130, Y=100, and Z=110) and to quote the luminance (200) separately. [The technical definition of luminance is avoided here. It is sufficient to regard it as the intensity (amount) of light, where light is considered in the psychophysical sense described at the beginning of this chapter.]

The foregoing discussion is concerned with color measurement in the case of light from luminous sources such as lamps. But what is done in the measurement of the colors of opaque and transparent objects? The situation is much the same. The color measurement is performed on the light coming from an illuminated opaque surface or being transmitted from a transparent surface. The color depends on the reflectance (or transmittance) characteristics of an object and on the characteristics of the light that falls on it. Thus, a specification of a surface color may be given by the tristimulus values X, Y, and Z and CIE ILL D_{65}. But, for opaque and transparent materials, Y has a *relative* meaning. For opaque materials, Y is the *luminance factor* (or *luminous reflectance*), which is the luminance of the surface relative to the luminance of an ideal white surface that has the same illumination and angle of view [6.3]. For transparent materials, Y refers to *luminous transmittance*.

Although colors can be specified by means of the CIE tristimulus values X, Y, and Z, it is rarely done. It is more meaningful to employ either chromaticity (x,y) or dominant wavelength and purity (discussed in the next section) than to employ X and Z. A CIE color specification based on chromaticity is written CIE(x,y,Y). The values of x and y, which are the fractional amounts of the imaginary red and green primaries in the mixture, are very easily calculated from the CIE tristimulus values, as described in Sect.6.2.

As in the case of real primaries (Sect.6.2), the chromaticities of the imaginary primaries occupy the corners of the triangular diagram, and the chromaticity of any color (real or imaginary) that results from their mixture is represented by one point plotted within the triangle or on one of its three sides. White produced by an equal mixture of the primaries is represented by its chromaticity at the center E, as it was in Fig.6.7.

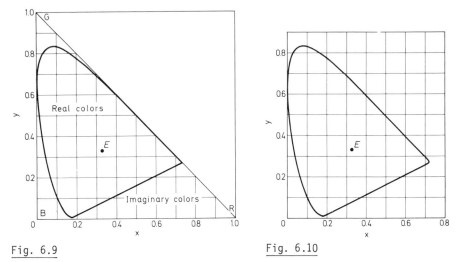

Fig. 6.9   Fig. 6.10

Fig. 6.9. CIE chromaticity diagram or Maxwell triangle (right triangle) based on the three imaginary primaries (from Fig.6.8)

Fig. 6.10. CIE (1931) chromaticity diagram as ordinarily presented

The chromaticities of all real colors fall within a tongue-shaped area or on its borders (Fig.6.9). The area outside the tongue-shaped area is the site of points that represent chromaticities of imaginary colors; it is therefore of no practical interest. For this reason, that area and the legs of the triangle are disregarded; in practice, only the tongue-shaped area is presented (Fig.6.10). This is the internationally accepted *CIE 1931 chromaticity diagram*.

Now let us consider more closely the general structure of the diagram while keeping the original triangle in mind (Fig.6.9). The top of the tongue-shaped area is the site of greens; the bottom-left area, blues; and the bottom-right area, reds. The chromaticities of all colors produced by monochromatic light are located along the curved edge of the tongue-shaped area. This curved edge or line is called the *spectrum locus*. Because monochromatic radiation is by definition light of single wavelength, the wavelength scale is sometimes indicated along the spectrum locus (Fig.6.12). The straight line (called the *purple line*) that borders the bottom of the tongue-shaped area connects the chromaticities for red (wavelength 700 nm) and blue (400 nm) and represents the chromaticities of their mixtures, which produce certain reds and the full range of purples, all of essentially 100% saturation. As mentioned earlier (Sect.4.3), colors that have purple hues, or hues of red associated with the purple line, are called *nonspectral colors*; all other chromatic colors are called *spectral colors*.

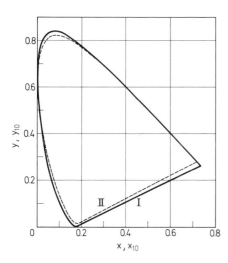

Fig. 6.11. CIE (1931) (x,y) chromaticity diagram (I) and CIE (1964) (x_{10}, y_{10}) chromaticity diagram (II). [Ref.2.3, Fig.2.17]; reprinted by permission of John Wiley & Sons, Inc.

The location of a chromaticity point reveals some information about the saturation of the color: the closer the point is to the spectrum locus or to the purple line, the higher is the saturation. Zero saturation is found in the region around E. More is said about this topic in the discussion of dominant wavelength (Sect.6.4).

The 1931 CIE chromaticity diagram is based on test data for a narrow angle of vision (2°) and is considered suitable in colorimetry for angles from 1° to 4° [Ref.5.13, p. 25]. An angle of 4° projected from an eye includes a disk 17 cm in diameter located at a distance of 2.5 m; an angle of 1° includes a disk of 4.4 cm diameter at the same distance. For an angle less than 4°, images obtained by looking directly at an object fall within a region called the *fovea*, which is the part of the eye's retina that permits the sharpest vision (Fig.2.1).

Because many color applications involve large angles of vision, in 1964 the CIE adopted a second chromaticity diagram based on a 10° angle of vision. This larger angle, when projected from the eye, includes a disk of diameter 44 cm at a distance of 2.5 m. There is a difference between the 1931 and 1964 diagrams (Fig.6.11) because, for a 10° angle, the image on the retina extends beyond the edge of the fovea, and consequently somewhat different color responses are obtained.

Although the notations in the 1931 system are X, Y, Z and x, y, z, those for the 1964 system are X_{10}, Y_{10}, Z_{10} and x_{10}, y_{10}, z_{10}. For color specifications based on the 1931 system, it is recommended to write CIE 1931(x,y,Y).

For those based on the 1964 system, write CIE 1964(x_{10},y_{10},Y_{10}). Most of the applications discussed in this book make use of the 1931 system. Two examples of specifications from a paper on artists' pigments by BARNES [5.7] and discussed in Sect.5.2 are: cadmium red, CIE 1931 (0.5375, 0.3402, 0.2078), CIE ILL C; madder lake, CIE 1931 (0.3985, 0.2756, 0.3355), CIE ILL C. When there is no doubt that the date 1931 is intended, it is usually omitted in a specification.

6.4 Dominant Wavelength and Purity

There is an acceptable way to specify color that is more descriptive than CIE (x,y,Y); it is favored in certain industries. The notation is given by CIE (λ_D,p_e,Y), where λ_D is the Greek letter lambda (with a subscript) used as the symbol for *dominant wavelength*, p_e is the *excitation purity*, or simply *purity*, and Y, as before, is either the luminance of the luminance factor.

An idea of what dominant wavelength and purity are can be gained from the two examples from the work of BARNES cited at the end of the previous section. The method requires the choice of a reference point on the chromaticity diagram, which characterizes the illumination that is applicable, in this case CIE ILL C (daylight). Point C in Fig.6.12 represents the chromaticity of CIE ILL C (Table 7.6), and point P represents the chromaticity of the cadmium red pigment. A straight line drawn from C through P intersects the spectrum locus at a point that represents the chromaticity of a color produced by a monochromatic radiation. The wavelength of that radiation provides the number called the *dominant wavelength*, in this case 605 nm. Because the wavelength of monochromatic radiation may be taken as an indicator of the hue of its perceived color, dominant wavelength, in psychophysics, is considered to be an approximate correlate of a color's perceived hue.

To determine the purity p_e, measure with a ruler (or otherwise) the distance between points C and P and divide it by the total length of the line, from C to the spectrum locus. The quotient, or fractional distance of P on the path from C to the spectrum locus, is the *purity*. Clearly, if the position of P on the line were varied from C to the spectrum locus, purity would increase from zero to 100%. For the cadmium red pigment the purity is 0.673 or 67.3% and the specification is given by CIE 1931 (λ_D=605 nm, p_e=67.3%, Y=0.208), CIE ILL C.

A second example is needed to illustrate what is done in the case of nonspectral colors. Point Q represents the chromaticity of the color of madder

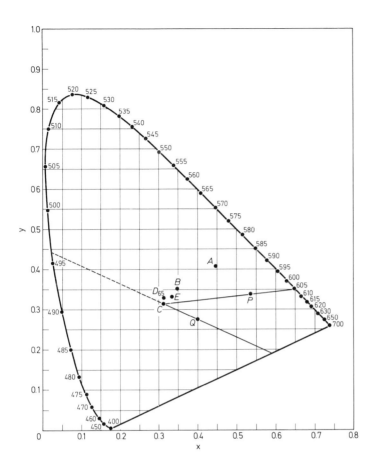

Fig. 6.12. CIE (1931) chromaticity diagram. The wavelength (in nanometers) of monochromatic light is indicated along the spectrum locus for use in determining the dominant wavelength or complementary wavelength of a color (see also Fig.7.2). The chromaticity point for a standard illuminant (CIE ILL A, B, C, and D_{65}) or that for equal-energy light (E) may be used as the reference point

lake pigment measured by BARNES (Fig.6.12). In this case, the line drawn from reference point C through Q intersects the purple line. The purity p_e is determined as described above: the distance from C to Q is divided by the length of the line drawn from C to the purple line. Here the purity is found to be 0.329 or 32.9%.

But how does one represent the hue? Monochromatic radiation cannot produce purples and purplish reds. For nonspectral colors, the line is extended in the opposite direction (see the dashed portion in Fig.6.12) to the spectrum locus, and the *complementary wavelength* λ_c is reported, in this case 496.5c nm (a "c" is always affixed to avoid confusion). The specification for madder lake is CIE 1931 (λ_c=496.5c nm, p_e=32.9%, Y=0.336), CIE ILL C.

In Fig.6.12, five points are indicated that can serve as reference points (Table 7.6). The points for CIE ILL C and CIE ILL D_{65} may be used for the determination of dominant wavelength (or complementary wavelength) for the specification of colors of objects illuminated by daylight. The point for CIE ILL A may be used for objects illuminated by incandescent lamps. In these two cases, the objects viewed are perceived as part of the environment. Point E is used when the color produced by light from a luminous object is being considered and also when an illuminated nonluminous object is viewed in sur- roundings that are significantly darker than the object. The chromaticity of the equal-energy source E is pertinent because it is considered neutral with respect to the dark field [Ref.6.4, p. 846]. Because the values for λ_D (or λ_c) and for p_e depend on which reference point is used, a precise color spec- ification must identify the illuminant that was used.

A color specification in terms of dominant (or complementary) wavelength and purity is sometimes preferred to the standard CIE(x,y,Y), because it sug- gests immediately a perceived hue and saturation. If we are given only the values for x and y, it is usually necessary to plot the point on the chroma- ticity diagram in order to grasp some idea of color quality. Another advan- tage arises in comparing two colors that do not differ much. Comparison of their values for x and y can lead to a rough idea of their differences, but given values for their λ_D (or λ_c) and p_e we can tell relatively quickly how they differ in hue and saturation [Ref.6.1, p. 118].

Purity is only an approximate correlate of perceived saturation. Although purity and perceived saturation increase from the reference point outwards, they do not necessarily increase by similar steps. If the colors of two paint samples have the same purity but different dominant wavelengths, it is not unusual for the perceived saturations to be different [Ref.2.1, p. 135]. Do- minant (or complementary) wavelength, although it is a useful indicator of perceived hue, is also not precise. For example, along a straight line of constant dominant wavelength from the reference point to the spectrum locus (or purple line), the perceived hue may vary significantly.

7. Diverse Applications of the CIE Chromaticity Diagram

7.1 Color Names for Lights

The CIE 1931 chromaticity diagram is primarily a tool for those concerned with colorimetry and color specification. There are, however, a number of other applications to which it may be put and which are relevant in art and design.

First of all, the CIE chromaticity diagram can serve as a kind of *color-name map* for lights. Kenneth L. KELLY has proposed the division of the diagram into color-name zones that form the map shown in Fig.7.1 [7.1,2]. The color names that he assigned are listed in Table 7.1. For the most part, the zones designate hue ranges. The color names do not show differences of satu-

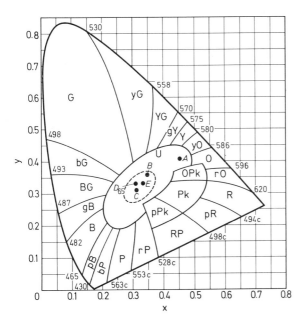

Fig. 7.1. K.L. Kelly's map for determining color names for light. (Modification of the figure in [7.1])

Table 7.1. Color names for lights (Fig.7.1) [7.1]

pB	Purplish Blue	O	Orange
B	Blue	OPk	Orange-Pink
gB	Greenish Blue	rO	Reddish Orange
BG	Blue-Green	Pk	Pink
bG	Bluish Green	R	Red
G	Green	pR	Purplish Red
yG	Yellowish Green	pPk	Purplish Pink
YG	Yellow-Green	RP	Red-Purple
gY	Greenish Yellow	rP	Reddish Purple
Y	Yellow	P	Purple
yO	Yellowish Orange	bP	Bluish Purple

ration, except by the inclusion of pinks, and do not vary when the luminance is changed.

In the large central oval area labeled U, no color names have been proposed. The hues of colors represented by the chromaticities in this zone vary in prominence from indefinite [Ref.2.4, p. 52] to faint. The color produced by light from a tungsten-filament incandescent lamp, typified by CIE ILL A (point A in Fig.7.1), could be said to be a faint yellowish orange.

KELLY's diagram shows point C at the center (for CIE ILL C) from which the zone lines radiate. In Fig.7.1, points have been added for illuminants CIE ILL D_{65} and CIE ILL B and for the equal-energy source E, to show the locations of their chromaticities within an added "sausage-shaped" area [Ref. 2.4, p. 51] (dashed line) that could be designated as the achromatic or white zone (Sect.7.4).

The large zone assigned to green and the relatively small zone to red does not mean that there are more greens than reds. If chromaticity points were plotted for colors of equal color difference and of equal luminance over the whole diagram, they would be found to be more densely spaced in the red zone than in the green zone (Sect.7.9). This nonuniform spacing is considered a disadvantage inherent in the CIE chromaticity diagram.

On KELLY's diagram, the wavelength scale for monochromatic radiation is shown along the spectrum locus. In Fig.7.1, this has been changed to show values of wavelength only at points where zone-division lines intersect the spectrum locus. These wavelength values are used to designate perceived hue ranges in the spectrum in Table 4.2.

KELLY's color-name zones are also useful as a quick and approximate means for identifying the colors of objects from their color specifications CIE (x,y,Y) [2.4]. It should be realized, however, that because the nomenclature is intended for lights, it does not include such color names as olive green

and brown. For example, at a chromaticity of (0.540, 0.410) the color of an
object is deep orange at a luminance factor Y = 0.20; strong brown at Y = 0.12;
and deep brown at Y = 0.03 [7.3]. For colored light of the same chromaticity,
however, the color would be orange, regardless of the luminance. A more sat-
isfactory method for designating names for the colors of materials, the ISCC-
NBS method [7.3], is discussed in Sect.8.8.

7.2 Determining Complementary Colors

The CIE chromaticity diagram can serve as a kind of *color circle* for identifying *complementary colors*. This is not surprising; we need only recall the
diametral placements of complementary colors in the Maxwell triangle and in
the Goethe color circle (Fig.6.6). The notion of complementary colors (Sect.
6.2) can be illustrated by additive color mixture. If two beams of light of
widely different hue can be adjusted in intensity so that their mixture will
produce a white disk on a white wall, the original colors are said to be complementary. Likewise, if the colors of two different papers are mixed, such
as when sectors of colored paper are viewed on a rapidly rotating disk (color
mixture by averaging), and if a neutral gray can be produced by adjusting
the areas of the sectors of the two colors, the two colors are said to be
complementary.

A straight *mixture line*, which connects the two points that represent the
chromaticities of the two colors, is the path on which all points fall that
represent the chromaticities of all possible mixtures of the two colors (either additive color mixture or mixture by averaging) (Sect.6.2). If the
straight mixture line passes through the central achromatic region (the approximate region shown by the dashed curve in Fig.7.1), then an achromatic
mixture is possible, indicating that the two colors are complementary. Because the boundary of the achromatic region is rather vague, the determination of whether colors are complementary or not is not a precise matter.
However, a complementary color can be determined precisely with respect to a
selected reference white, for example, point E (equal-energy light source)
in the case of colored light, or point C (CIE ILL C) in the case of illuminated objects.

The chromaticities of the colors of two monochromatic beams M (494 nm) and
N (640 nm) are indicated in Fig.7.2. Their mixture line passes through point
E, showing that the colors are complementary with respect to the equal-energy
source E. The dashed line that connects points S and K shows that the colors

60

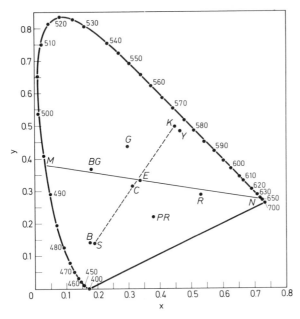

Fig. 7.2. CIE (1931) chromaticity diagram used in determination of comple-mentary colors

Table 7.2. K.L. Kelly's list of colors of maximum contrast [7.4]

Color selection number	ISCC-NBS color name	ISCC-NBS centroid number	Luminance factor Y	Munsell value V
1	white	263	0.90	9.5
2	black	267	0.0094	0.8
3	vivid yellow	82	0.59	8.0
4	strong purple	218	0.14	4.3
5	vivid orange	48	0.36	6.5
6	very light blue	180	0.57	7.9
7	vivid red	11	0.11	3.9
8	grayish yellow	90	0.46	7.2
9	medium gray	265	0.24	5.4
10	vivid green	139	0.19	4.9
11	strong purplish pink	247	0.40	6.8
12	strong blue	178	0.13	4.1
13	strong yellowish pink	26	0.43	7.0
14	strong violet	207	0.10	3.7
15	vivid orange yellow	66	0.48	7.3
16	strong purplish red	255	0.15	4.4
17	vivid greenish yellow	97	0.63	8.2
18	strong reddish brown	40	0.070	3.1
19	vivid yellow green	115	0.40	6.8
20	deep yellowish brown	75	0.070	3.1
21	vivid reddish orange	34	0.24	5.4
22	dark olive green	126	0.036	2.2

S and K, a blue and a yellow, are complementary with respect to CIE ILL C. These are the colors of two paint samples discussed in Sects.7.7 and 7.8. In color mixture by averaging, such as for color samples on a rapidly rotating disk, the dashed line indicates their mixtures. But, as is shown later, the points that represent various subtractive mixtures of them would fall on a curve that would not pass through the achromatic zone (Fig.7.12). No mixture of the two paints can produce neutral gray. The question of whether the colors of materials are complementary is answered by whether or not the straight line (for color mixture by averaging) passes through or close to the reference point.

The chromaticities of the colors employed in the Goethe color circle in Plate I (color plate) are identified by six points in Fig.7.2. The complementary pairs are B, deep blue (179), and Y, vivid yellow (82); G, dark yellowish green (137), and PR, deep purplish red (256); and BG, strong bluish green (160), and R, vivid red (11) (ISCC-NBS color names and centroid numbers, Sect.8.8 [7.3]). When straight lines are drawn to connect these pairs of points, they are found to pass rather close to point C.

In the above discussion, complementary colors are taken to be those that can produce white or neutral gray by additive color mixture or color mixture by averaging. This is the psychophysical concept of complementary colors. In psychology, the word "complementary" is sometimes used somewhat differently to describe the colors that are perceived in two different visual phenomena, afterimages and simultaneous contrast (which includes colored shadows) [Ref. 2.4, p. 224].

From a collection of 267 color chips (the ISCC-NBS centroid colors, Sect. 8.8) that samples the full gamut of surface colors, KELLY has selected 22 colors of maximum contrast for use in color coding, for example in safety and commercial applications [7.4]. The colors, identified by their ISCC-NBS color names and centroid numbers, are to be considered in the order shown in Table 7.2. Each color contrasts maximally in hue or lightness with the one immediately preceding it in the list and contrasts significantly with earlier ones. [The first nine colors provide maximum contrast not only for persons with normal color vision but also for those with color blindness (red-green deficiency).] The numerical values for luminance factor and Munsell Value (Sect.8.4) given in Table 7.2 indicate the variations of lightness. Figs.7.3 and 7.4 show lines that join the chromaticity points for the colors, in the order listed. The closeness of a line to the point for CIE ILL C indicates the degree to which a pair of colors is complementary in the psychophysical sense. Those pairs of colors that are not complementary predominantly exhibit lightness contrasts.

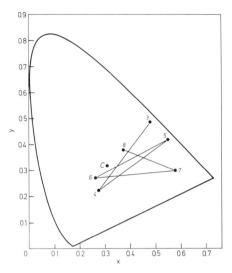 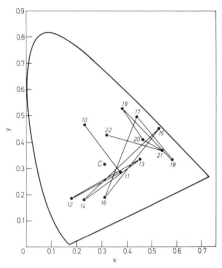

Fig. 7.3. Color samples of maximum contrast (samples 3-8, Table 7.2)[7.4]

Fig. 7.4. Color samples of maximum contrast (samples 10-22, Table 7.2)[7.4]

7.3 Colors Obtainable by Mixing Light

The CIE chromaticity diagram can serve in a way that should be of interest to those who work with colored lights, lasers, and phosphors (for example, color-television phosphors) as art media. It can be used to predict the chromaticity of colors obtainable by mixing two or more light beams of different color. (The CIE chromaticity diagram is sometimes called a *mixture diagram* [Ref.6.4, p. 842].) If, for example, purplish blue light Q is mixed with red light R by combining the beams from two projectors, the chromaticity of the resulting color is located at some point on the straight *mixture line* that connects the chromaticity points Q and R (Fig.7.5).

The location of the chromaticity point for the color of the mixture on the mixture line depends on the relative amounts of Q and R. For color-mixture calculations, the amount of each of the two beams is given by the measured luminance Y divided by the chromaticity coefficient y [Ref.2.2, p. 236; 7.5]. If, for beam Q, $Y = 30$ and $y = 0.15$ (see Fig.7.5), and, for beam R, $Y = 90$ and $y = 0.30$, then the amount of Q is 30/0.15, or 200, and that for R is 90/0.30, or 300. The amount of mixture is 200 + 300, or 500, and the fractional amount of R in the mixture is 300/500, or 0.60. The mixture is predominantly red: the mixture point M is located on the mixture line 0.60 (or 60%) of the way

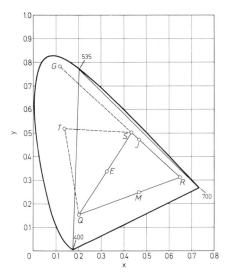

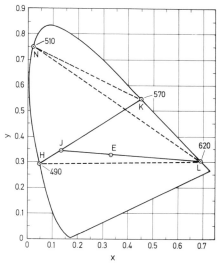

Fig. 7.5. Chromaticity gamuts available for mixtures of beams of colored light

Fig. 7.6. Production of white light from three beams of colored light

from Q to R. The amounts of Q and R are the sums of their tristimulus values: $X + Y + Z$.

If the red light is mixed with the greenish yellow light represented by point S, the gamut available is represented by the mixture line that connects R and S. The extension of the mixture line up to G in the green region of the diagram demonstrates that yellow J can be produced by the additive mixture of red R and green G (Sect.5.6).

The mixture line between Q and S represents the gamut of mixtures obtainable by mixing purplish blue and greenish yellow light. Because the line passes through point E, the two colors are complementary with respect to equal-energy source E.

Although the gamut of chromaticities of colors obtainable by the additive mixture of two beams of light of different colors is given by a straight mixture line, the gamut available with three beams of different hues is given by a triangle. In Fig.7.5, one such gamut is indicated by the triangular area formed by joining points Q, R, and S. The gamut can be increased by extending the area to reach other points outside the triangle. For example, if point T is added, representing a fourth beam of another hue, the new gamut is given by the area bounded by four lines formed by joining successively points Q, R, S, T, and Q.

The large gamut that may be produced by mixtures of three monochromatic light beams (the Hardy-Wurzburg triangle), to which reference is made in Sect.5.9, is illustrated by the triangle formed by connecting the points on the spectrum locus labeled 700, 535, and 400 nm [Ref.2.2, p. 238]. Because monochromatic light can be produced by lasers or can be isolated readily from laser beams consisting of light of several wavelengths, lasers offer a rich potential source of large gamuts of colors. Unfortunately, however, costly equipment may be required to produce such mixtures, and provisions may have to be made to overcome serious safety hazards.

It should be recalled that the CIE 1931 chromaticity diagram is applicable to angles of vision between $1°$ and $4°$ (Sect.6.3). Those interested in artistic applications of colored light may need to consider using the 1964 CIE chromaticity diagram (Fig.6.11) if accuracy is an important consideration.

Mixing of colored light emitted by television phosphors is discussed briefly in Sect.7.8.

7.4 Light Called "White Light"

Light that produces an achromatic (hueless) visual response is commonly called *white light*. Measurements show that light that produces such a response is not characterized by a unique chromaticity, but rather by a rather vaguely defined gamut of chromaticities suggested by a sausage-shaped area whose approximate length is indicated by 4000 and 10,000 K (color temperatures) [Ref. 2.4, p. 51] in Fig.7.15. The dashed line in Fig.7.1 is intended to outline approximately the sausage-shaped area. Light represented by points within that area (E and CIE ILL B, C, and D_{65}) evokes an achromatic visual sensation; it is white. But light from an ordinary incandescent (tungsten-filament) lamp (typified by CIE ILL A) does not; it is not white.

Because sunlight can be dispersed into a spectrum of practically all wavelengths in the range from 380 to 780 nm, it is often erroneously assumed that white light necessarily is a mixture of light of all wavelengths in the range. But it should be remembered that white light of a given chromaticity can be produced by many mixtures whose wavelength composition does not include all wavelengths. An extreme example is provided by a mixture whose wavelength composition is given by two wavelengths, such as the two complementary monochromatic beams M and N indicated in Fig.7.2.

It is easy to demonstrate how three beams of monochromatic light, H (490 nm, blue-green), K (570 nm, greenish yellow) and L (620 nm, red)(Fig.7.6), can be combined to produce a beam of white light (represented by E). The demonstration may be begun by combining beams H and K to produce the mixture J. Then beam L is added to J to produce the final mixture E. The resulting white light is composed of three wavelengths. A similar demonstration could be made for the production of white light from four, five, or any number of different monochromatic beams.

On the basis of the discussion in Sect.7.3, beams H, K, and L can be expected to provide a combination that forms a white mixture E, because the triangle formed by connecting the three points *encloses* E. On the other hand, it is evident that monochromatic beams K, L, and N cannot produce a white mixture (Fig.7.6).

The fact that mixtures, such as one of H, K, and L, match daylight precisely does not mean that the perceived color of an object illuminated by daylight and by each of its matching mixtures will be the same. Generally, the color will be different under each illumination. Only in the case of a white object, which reflects almost all of the light it receives, is it certain that the color (white) will not change (this is the condition under which the match is made). But a green vase in daylight is not green when illuminated by the white mixture of beams H, K, and L, because no light is provided in the wavelength region from 500 to 560 nm for scattering to the eye. Matching white mixtures of equal luminance (metamers) may be of potential interest in art (Sect.5.5). In the above illustration, a mixture of three monochromatic beams was employed. But, generally, there is no reason why the beams should be monochromatic.

In general, however, people prefer lighting in which objects (especially their faces) appear in their "natural" coloring. This subject is dealt with under the designation *color rendering* in the domain of illumination engineering. The *color rendering index* measures the degree to which the perceived colors of objects illuminated by a lamp, for example, conform to the colors of the same objects under standard illumination, for specified viewing conditions [7.6,7].

7.5 The Color Limits for Materials (Paints, Inks, Dyes, ect.)

The CIE chromaticity diagram can serve as a maximum-gamut map that defines the ultimate limits of the gamuts of all colors. Of course, practical limits, imposed by the availability and cost of pigments, dyes, and light sources,

restrict what an artist or designer can employ, but these limits are pushed
back as technology advances toward the limits of what is possible.

The ultimate limits of the gamut of all colors produced by light from luminous sources are set by the tongue-shaped spectrum locus and the straight
purple line on the chromaticity diagram. These limits are not modified by
the luminance Y within normal conditions for perceiving colors.

It was pointed out in Sect.6.3 that the CIE chromaticity diagram applies
not only to the colors produced by light coming directly from luminous sources
but also to the colors of objects, because color measurement is performed on
the light received after it is scattered from or passes through the objects.
The important difference is that *only certain regions* of the tongue-shaped
area are available for representing the chromaticities of the colors of scattered or transmitted light — light that remains after selective absorption
occurs in nonluminous, nonfluorescent objects. In these cases, the locations
and shapes of the regions are related to the luminance factor Y. The limits
of the regions have been determined precisely for CIE ILL A and CIE ILL C by
the psychophysicist D.L. MacADAM and are known in the U.S.A. as the MacAdam
limits [7.8]. The German mineralogist S. RÖSCH reported some work on the subject somewhat earlier (1928), and in German color literature his name is associated with the same concept [Ref.3.7, p. 341; Ref.5.3, Fig.14.09(2)].

The condition for which the luminance factor is taken equal to 1.0 (Y=1.0)
represents whiteness equal to that of a standard white surface. It represents
total reflection and scattering of incident light without selective absorption and color change. This is approached by snow and finely ground table
salt, for example. Similarly, a clear glass would be colorless (Y=1.0) if light
passes through it without appreciable reduction or change of wavelength composition. Thus, for a situation where $Y = 1.0$, the chromaticity of the color
by reflection and scattering is identical to the chromaticity of the color of
the incident light. The discussion below concerns the MacAdam limits in the
case of daylight illumination (CIE ILL C), in which the only color that can
be produced at $Y = 1.0$ is white. This condition is represented by point C on
the chromaticity diagram, the location of the chromaticity for CIE ILL C.

A luminance factor below 1.0 signifies that part of the light received by
the object is absorbed; the remainder is scattered and reflected. At the same
chromaticity (point C) and at luminance factors below 1.0, in place of white
there is the achromatic gamut of neutral grays. Thus, at $Y = 0.60$, the color
is light gray; at $Y = 0.25$, medium gray; at $Y = 0.10$, dark gray; and below
$Y = 0.05$, essentially black [7.3]. It should be noted that a luminance factor

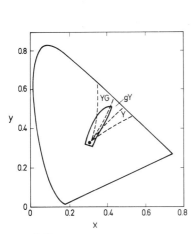

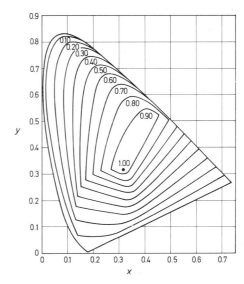

Fig. 7.7   Fig. 7.8

Fig. 7.7. Chromaticity limit (MacAdam limit) for colors of nonfluorescent materials, luminance factor Y = 0.95 (CIE ILL C) [7.8]. ISCC-NBS color-name zones: Y (yellow), gY (greenish yellow), and YG (yellow green) [7.3]

Fig. 7.8. Chromaticity limits (MacAdam limits) for colors of nonfluorescent materials. Luminance-factor range from Y = 0 to Y = 1.00. (Based on [7.8])

of 0.60, for example, implies 40% absorption of psychophysical light (perceived light), not a 40% absorption of received radiant energy (Sect.6.1).

The previous paragraph concerns achromatic colors at various levels of luminance factor, when an object is illuminated by a source typified by CIE ILL C. The next step is to consider the gamuts of colors possible at the various levels of luminance factor. These are the regions bounded by the MacAdam limits. (Only nonfluorescent objects are considered in this section.)

At luminance factor Y = 1.0, the region of the chromaticity diagram available for the colors of objects is restricted to a point, point C — that is, to one color only: white. (Note that by giving the chromaticity, the luminance factor, and the illuminant CIE ILL C one specifies the color.)

The small region on the chromaticity diagram defined by the MacAdam limit at Y = 0.95 is shown in Fig.7.7. Also indicated are color zones (dashed lines) based on the color-name system [7.3] described in Sect.8.8. Outside the MacAdam limit no colors with Y = 0.95 are possible for nonfluorescent objects.

When the luminance factor is decreased, the gamuts of possible colors, described by the MacAdam limits, expand. Fig.7.8 shows the MacAdam limits at

Table 7.3. Colors of samples shown in Plates II and V (color plates)

Sample number	ISCC-NBS color name and centroid number	Luminance factor, Y	Munsell notation Hue Value/Chroma
1	strong bluish green (160)	0.342	4.5BG 6.34/8.9
2	brilliant blue (177)	0.301	3.0PB 6.00/10.0
3	light purplish blue (199)	0.332	5.0PB 6.26/6.8
4	light purple (222)	0.320	6.0P 6.16/6.4
5	light reddish purple (240)	0.251	0.4RP 5.54/8.6
6	deep purplish pink (248)	0.327	4.3RP 6.22/11.5
7	deep pink (3)	0.329	5.2R 6.24/7.2
8	moderate reddish orange (37)	0.299	7.0R 5.99/10.2
9	deep pink (3)	0.280	2.5R 5.82/13.9
10	strong reddish orange (35)	0.278	8.5R 5.80/12.6
11	strong orange (50)	0.301	5.0YR 6.00/10.0
12	vivid orange (48)	0.301	2.5YR 6.00/16.0
13	deep yellow (85)	0.301	5.0Y 6.00/10.0
14	dark yellow (88)	0.301	5.0Y 6.00/6.0
15	dark grayish yellow (91)	0.301	5.0Y 6.00/4.0
16	light grayish olive (109)	0.301	5.0Y 6.00/2.0
17	greenish gray (155)	0.301	5.0GY 6.00/1.0
18	strong yellow green (117)	0.301	5.0GY 6.00/10.0
19	vivid yellowish green (129)	0.301	10.0GY 6.00/12.0
20	brilliant green (140)	0.301	5.0G 6.00/10.0
21	brilliant greenish blue (168)	0.301	2.5B 6.00/8.0
22	pale blue (185)	0.301	2.5B 6.00/2.0

eleven levels of Y from Y = 1.00 (a point) down to Y = 0. At Y = 0.90 the limited region is approximately rectangular, as it is at Y = 0.95 (Fig.7.7). At Y = 0.95 the gamut is rather small, being limited primarily to the yellows from pale to brilliant and vivid. At Y = 0.90, the gamut includes yellow greens and more yellows. And so it continues as Y decreases. At Y = 0.10, the gamut is very large; but, of course, at such a low luminance factor, the colors are dark. At Y = 0 the MacAdam limit coincides with the spectrum locus and purple line of the chromaticity diagram, and the colors, for all hues, are of maximum darkness, black.

Plate II (color plate) shows a number of glossy samples that have luminance factors equal to about Y = 0.30. The color samples are intended to provide a varied display at one level of luminance factor and to show the distribution of colors on the chromaticity diagram. Some of the samples (1-10) were cut from specimens in a commercial pigment catalog [5.14], and others (11-22) were cut from standard Munsell color chips. Data relevant to the samples are given in Table 7.3. Faithful reproduction of the colors (originally accurately represented by their designations) cannot be assured in Plate II.

The MacAdam limits apply to colors that are not diluted by surface-reflected light (Sect.5.2). Calculations of limits have been published that

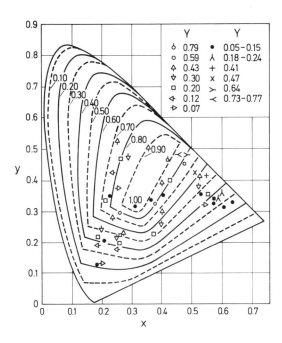

Fig. 7.9. Chromaticities of the colors of acrylic artists' paints in relation to the chromaticity limits (MacAdam limits). Points indicated by circles and triangles [7.10]; other points [7.11]

take into account surface reflection of 4% of the incident light. The resulting limits are decreased significantly, an effect that should be remembered when matte paint colors are being considered [7.9].

Figure 7.9 shows the chromaticity points for the colors of samples of artists' acrylic paints based on data published by one manufacturer. Not shown are points for very dark paints for which the luminance factor Y is below 0.05. The plot is interesting because it demonstrates the general distribution of the hues. It also provides an example of the application of the MacAdam limits. The position of a chromaticity point for the color of a paint can be compared with its MacAdam limit at the same level of luminance factor. Paints that have luminance factors of about 0.20 (points shown as squares) are compared on the chromaticity diagram with the MacAdam limit for Y = 0.20. Because these particular paints are known to contain pigments of good permanency, the proximity of their chromaticity points to the limit gives some indication of the possible improvements of color saturation that might be hoped for in new stable pigments. Of course, allowance should be made for the fact that water-base acrylic paints produce matte films and that, if they were made glossy by the addition of a layer of clear acrylic lacquer, their color saturations would increase and their chromaticity points would be closer to the MacAdam limit.

7.6 Fluorescent Paints and Dyes

The MacAdam limits (Sect.7.5) apply only to the colors of nonfluorescent objects. The chromaticity points for the colors of fluorescent paints are commonly located outside the MacAdam limits, but they are never located outside the boundaries of the tongue-shaped chromaticity diagram — that is, in the territory of imaginary colors (Sect.6.3, Fig.6.9). An example of a point that falls outside the MacAdam limit for Y = 0.55 is specified by CIE(0.640, 0.355, 0.553), CIE ILL C [5.11]; it is given by point A in Fig.7.10. The color of a nonfluorescent paint, used as a standard safety color, having about the same chromaticity (the same point A) is appreciably darker (Y=0.15). It is well within the MacAdam limit shown for Y = 0.15.

A number of fluorescent dyes are commercially available. As mentioned earlier (Sect.5.4), products sold as fluorescent pigments are generally dyes dissolved in a hardened plastic base that is ground to a powder. Unfortunately, presently available fluorescent materials have inferior lightfastness. However, by use of ample amounts in paints and by restricting exposure to light, the life of fluorescent paintings can be extended appreciably.

It is hoped that fluorescent colorants of great variety will eventually be developed. EVANS mentioned the interesting possibility of extending the range of Munsell samples beyond the MacAdam limits by use of fluorescent pigments [3.4]. His studies of perception showed that the nonfluorescent region passes continuously into the fluorescent region. Fluorescent colors that are not fluorent might be used to fill in some gaps.

7.7 Mixing Paints

The CIE chromaticity diagram provides a convenient way for predicting the chromaticities of the colors of mixtures of light (Sect.7.3). The fact that the mixture lines are straight (additive color mixture), and require only two points to establish them, accounts for the ease of the method. In the case of mixing pigments or dyes (subtractive color mixture), however, the mixture lines are very frequently curved and three or more points must be

Table 7.4. Identification of pigment mixtures and colors of samples shown in Plate III (color plate)

C/W Pigment weight ratio Colored(C) White(W) [b]	ISCC-NBS color name	Luminance factor Y	Munsell notation Hue Value/Chroma
[a]1-A 100/0	strong greenish yellow	0.503	9.0Y 7.47/10.5
1-B 50/50	light greenish yellow	0.702	0.5GY 8.59/7.7
1-C 10/90	pale greenish yellow	0.824	2.0GY 9.17/3.8
2-A 100/0	moderate yellow	0.560	1.5Y 7.82/16.8
2-B 33/67	brilliant yellow	0.652	2.5Y 8.33/10.9
2-C 5/95	pale yellow	0.758	4.0Y 8.87/4.9
3-A 100/0	vivid reddish orange	0.169	10.0R 4.67/16.4
3-B 33/67	strong reddish orange	0.278	8.5R 5.80/12.6
3-C 5/95	strong yellowish pink	0.500	7.5R 7.46/7.2
4-A 100/0	deep reddish brown	0.043	10.0R 2.41/11.8
4-B 33/67	strong red	0.103	2.5R 3.72/12.8
4-C 10/90	strong purplish red	0.197	9.0R 4.99/12.0
5-A 100/0	very deep red	0.0138	8.2R 1.12/7.6
5-B 25/75	deep purplish red	0.0875	3.8RP 3.45/10.4
5-C 5/95	light reddish purple	0.251	0.4RP 5.54/8.6
6-A 100/0	blackish purple	0.006	1.5P 0.47/1.7
6-B 33/67	strong blue	0.085	6.0PB 3.40/9.0
6-C 5/95	light purplish blue	0.332	5.0PB 6.26/6.8
7-A 100/0	very dark greenish blue	0.004	4.0B 0.31/4.3
7-B 33/67	strong bluish green	0.121	2.0BG 4.01/10.4
7-C 5/95	brilliant bluish green	0.342	4.5BG 6.34/8.9

[a]Pigments: 1, zinc yellow; 2, chrome yellow medium; 3, molybdate orange; 4, bon red dark; 5, "Monastral" violet R (quinacridone); 6, indanthrone blue lake; 7, "Monastral" green (phthalocyanine) [5.14]
[b]Titanium white [5.14]

provided to establish them on the chromaticity diagram. Plate III (color plate) shows sets of four chromaticity points that represent a white pigment (titanium white), a colored pigment, and two mixtures of colored and white pigments. The mixture line for each series terminates at point C (CIE ILL C) which closely represents the chromaticity of the white. The color samples shown were cut from glossy specimens in a commercial pigment catalog [5.14]. The identification of each sample and relevant information are presented in Table 7.4.

The mixture lines in Plate III show the changes of hue (roughly represented by dominant, or complementary, wavelength) and of saturation (roughly represented by purity) when a white pigment is added to a colored pigment. Of particular interest is series 6, which example shows increase of purity when two pigments are mixed (from point 6-A to point 6-B). After reaching a maximum

Table 7.5. Identification of yellow and blue pigment mixtures and the colors of samples shown in Plate IV (color plate)

	K/B Pigment weight ratio Yellow(K)[a] Blue(B)[b]	ISCC-NBS color names	Lumi- nance factor Y	Munsell notation Hue Value/Chroma
I-A	56/44	very dark bluish green	0.014	2.0BG 1.75/4.6
I-B	64/36	very dark bluish green	0.018	10.0G 1.39/6.2
I-C	75/25	very dark green	0.029	6.5G 1.90/6.9
I-D	80/20	deep green	0.038	4.5G 2.26/7.4
I-E	89/11	deep yellowish green	0.067	2.0G 3.03/8.3
I-F	93/7	deep yellowish green	0.094	1.0G 3.58/8.3
I-G	98/2	strong yellow green	0.189	7.5GY 4.90/9.4
K	100/0	vivid yellow	0.484	6.5Y 7.35/12.5

[a]Shading yellow (chrome yellow) [5.14]

[b]Milori blue (iron blue) [5.14]

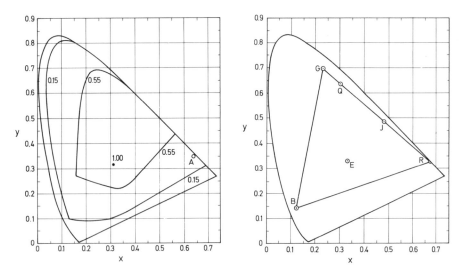

Fig. 7.10   Fig. 7.11

Fig. 7.10. Example of the chromaticity (A) of the color of a fluorescent paint that is located outside the chromaticity limits (MacAdam limits) at luminance factor Y = 0.55 [5.11]

Fig. 7.11. Chromaticity gamut of colors available with three television phosphors: red (R), green (G), and blue (B) (U.S. Standard, 1951) [7.13]

purity, shown by the hairpin turn, the purity decreases on further mixture with white pigment. The change of lightness on dilution with white is suggested by the tabulated values of the luminance factor Y (Table 7.4).

Plate IV (color plate) shows several types of mixture lines obtained from mixtures of pigments. Mixture lines I, II, and III represent sets of mixtures of two pigments, neither of which is white. The samples shown for mixture line I are identified in Table 7.5. The tabulated color names show the wide range of green hues available when the two pigments are mixed.

Curve II in Plate IV, shown by EVANS [Ref.2.2, Fig.18.7], is the mixture line for zinc yellow J and deep cadmium red R artists' oil paints. The mixture line given by curve III was shown in an article by JONES on artists' pigments employed in the past [Ref.7.12, Fig.12]. It represents the broad gamut of greens obtained in oil by mixing pigments Prussian blue P and lead chromate (chrome yellow) K. The mixture line demonstrates that, although the chromaticity points Q, C (CIE ILL C), and K all lie on a straight line (not shown) and, hence, colors K and Q are complementary, no mixture of the pigments on a palette will produce a neutral gray. JONES points out that the pigment mixtures represented in this range enabled 19th century painters for the first time to represent closely the greens found in nature. Curve IV from the same article [Ref.7.12, Fig.7] is a hairpin mixture line for Prussian blue P and white lead C in oil; it resembles the mixture line for samples 6-A, 6-B, and 6-C in Plate III.

These illustrations show that, even when the chromaticities of the colors of two pigments are known, the chromaticities of the colors of their mixtures cannot always be predicted accurately.

7.8 Color Television and Pointillistic Painting

The visual mixing of colors that occurs when color television or pointillistic paintings are viewed is described briefly in Sect.5.8. It is important to recognize that the result of visually mixing two colors is, in such cases, represented by straight mixture lines on the chromaticity diagram. Thus, in color television, in which rays of green G and red R light are emitted simultaneously, in one kind of set (or very rapidly, in sequence, in another kind of set), from tiny neighboring G and R phosphor dots on the screen, the chromaticity of the resulting uniformly mixed color is represented by a point on the straight mixture line that connects the points that represent G and R on the chromaticity diagram (Fig.7.11). The exact location of the point on the line, such as that for yellow J (Fig.7.1), is determined by the relative amounts of G and R in the mixture. If a yellowish green Q were desired, then the amount of G would have to be greater than the amount of R.

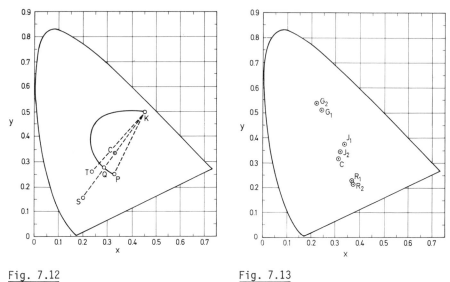

Fig. 7.12   Fig. 7.13

Fig. 7.12. Mixture lines for mixtures of Prussian blue (P) and chrome yellow (K) pigments: subtractive color mixture (curved line); color mixture by averaging (pointillistic painting) (straight dashed lines)

Fig. 7.13. Chromaticities of two pairs of colors of equal color difference (G$_1$ and G$_2$; R$_1$ and R$_2$) at constant luminance factor (Y=0.20) and of the color of a paint sample before (J$_1$) and after (J$_2$) fading with no change of luminance factor (Y=0.893)

The full gamut of chromaticities available by use of the three television phosphors, B (blue), G (green), and R (red), in Fig.7.11 is represented by the area within the three straight lines that form the triangle (Sect.7.3). White light, such as that represented by the equal-energy source E, can be produced by a mixture of appropriate relative amounts of blue, green, and red light.

The chromaticity diagram is pertinent to pointillistic painting, not only to identify the colors of different hues obtainable by visual color mixing but also to determine which color pairs or triads can lead to drab grayish colors. For example, a straight mixture line that passes through the central region of the chromaticity diagram warns of the possibility of gray mixtures and colors of low saturation. In Sect.7.7 comment was made on the interesting range of green colors obtainable by subtractive color mixture of Prussian blue and chrome yellow paints (curve III, Plate IV). In Fig.7.12 the curved mixture line is shown again to emphasize how it avoids the central region near point C. If, however, these two paints were applied to a canvas in a pointillistic manner, then a straight mixture line between points P and K would be followed. These colors are essentially complementary; the mixture line passes rather close to C. Therefore, unless there is a preponderance of either yellow or blue, an area painted in this manner would have a dull gray-ish appearance. Although a painter would probably not consider juxtaposing chrome yellow K and very dark, undiluted Prussian blue P dots, Fig.7.12 shows that dots of Prussian blue tints S or T (from curve IV in Plate IV) would also result in mixture lines that pass through the region that represents gray or grayish colors.

7.9 Color Differences

In industry, not only is the measurement of color important but also the mea-surement of color difference. The reason is that when a manufacturer agrees to produce a paint or an object painted in a certain color, he is often ex-pected to produce a color that will match a specified color within a stated tolerance of variation. The smaller the tolerance, the more difficult is his task.

Unfortunately color differences cannot be measured as distances on the CIE chromaticity diagram. One of the major criticisms of the diagram is that it is not uniform [Ref.6.1, pp. 108,178]. A large region of the diagram is occupied by greens, whereas the reds, purples, and blues are crowded into com-paratively small regions. This nonuniformity is illustrated in Fig.7.13. Points G_1 and G_2 represent the chromaticities of two greens of the same green hue. Their perceived color difference is equal to the perceived difference between two red-purples R_1 and R_2 of the same red-purple hue. The luminance factor for the four colors is the same, $Y = 0.20$. Although the color differ-ences are the same, the distance measured between points G_1 and G_2 is three times that between points R_1 and R_2. Clearly, distances measured on the CIE chromaticity diagram are not appropriate as measures of color differences.

In publications about color measurements published in the U.S.A. since 1940, there are numerous references to the *NBS unit* (sometimes called the *judd*) for designating small color differences. A color variation of one NBS unit represents about what is customarily tolerated in commerce [7.14]. One NBS unit is equivalent to a color difference that is approximately five just-perceptible color differences. (The Munsell equivalents are given in Sect. 8.4.) Numerical values for color differences in NBS units may be calculated from the CIE tristimulus values X, Y, and Z determined for each pair of colors [2.3; Ref.7.15, p. 292].

In the literature on the subject of color published during the years 1960 to 1975, there are discussions of a number of other proposed formulas for calculating color differences [Ref.5.13, p. 45; 7.16]. One formula used for calculating color differences, the *ANLAB(40)* formula [Ref.7.15, p. 12], has enjoyed rather wide acceptance, particularly in the British textile industry [7.17,18]. More recently, a simplified modification of the ANLAB(40) formula was recommended by the CIE. This modification, called *CIELAB(1976)*, is recommended for universal use (textiles, paints, plastics, etc.) [7.19-21]. The formula provides for the calculation of color differences from two sets of tristimulus values X, Y, and Z [Ref.7.15, p. 106]. Approximately, one ANLAB (40) unit [or one CIELAB(1976) unit] is equivalent to one NBS unit or five just-perceptible differences [7.22].

The CIELAB(1976) formula is recommended primarily for object colors. Another formula, *CIELUV* (1976), is recommended for expressing color differences in lighting, photography, television, and the graphic arts, whenever the chromaticities of the colors in question are also of interest [Ref.7.15, p. 107; 7.21].

As an instance of color-difference measurements that are important to artists and designers, the H.W. LEVISON report (published in 1976) on the lightfastness of numerous artists' pigments should be noted [5.1]. LEVISON determined the CIE tristimulus values X, Y, and Z of the colors of paint samples (containing the pigments) before and after exposing them to light. Because there was no internationally adopted color-difference formula at the time of his investigation, he reported his results in two ways, using two formulas, one of which was the ANLAB(40) color-difference formula. Using the ANLAB(40) color-difference results, he calculated a permanency rating for the various pigments.

Most of the pigments studied by LEVISON exhibited changes of both chromaticity and luminance factor after exposure to light. In Fig.7.13 the chromaticity of a yellow acrylic paint sample before (J_1) and after (J_2) several months of exposure to sunshine (in Ohio) is presented (Y=0.893). The sample (Hansa 10G, tint) is one of a number for which the chromaticity changed, but the luminance factor Y did not. The color change expressed in ANLAB(40) color units is 12.7; the resulting permanency rating is 3.2. (The permanency-rating scale extends from zero for a marginally acceptable lightfastness for the fine arts to 10 for 100% lightfastness.)

7.10 Color Temperature

Very frequently in the current literature on color the term *color temperature* is encountered, or its equivalent, *blackbody temperature*, in particular with reference to light from lamps. To understand the meaning of the term, consider the change of perceived color in a tiny hole in a piece of iron heated in a furnace. First a temperature is reached at which the hole becomes a dull red. When the temperature is increased further, it becomes a reddish orange and finally orange when the iron begins to melt (1535°C). If a hole in liquid iron could be observed when it is heated to its boiling point (3000°C), its color would approach white.

The path of the points that represent chromaticities of the iron as it is heated follows rather closely the dashed curved line shown in Fig.7.14 which starts on the right of the CIE chromaticity diagram. The portion of the chromaticity diagram shown as a box containing the curve is reproduced on a larger scale in Fig.7.15 to show detail better. The curve is called the *color-temperature curve*, or sometimes the *blackbody locus* or the *planckian locus*.

In science and technology, high temperatures such as those mentioned in the foregoing are often reported in kelvins, K (formerly in degrees Kelvin, °K), instead of in degrees Centigrade, °C [Ref.7.15, p. 246]. The number 273 is added to a temperature given in degrees Centigrade in order to obtain the value in kelvins. Thus a temperature reported as 3000°C is represented equally well by 3273 K, and a temperature given roughly as 4000°C is represented as well by 4300 K.

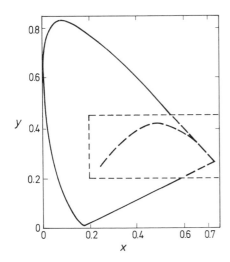

Fig. 7.14. Color-temperature curve (curved dashed line)

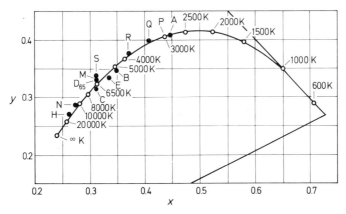

Fig. 7.15. Color-temperature curve. Enlargement of a portion of Fig.7.14, showing the full range of the color-temperature curve in kelvins K. Chromaticity points are shown for CIE ILL A,B,C, and D_{65} [Ref.2.3, p. 166]; equal-energy light (E); light from 40-watt standard warm white (P), white (Q), standard cool white (R), and daylight (S) fluorescent lamps [Ref.3.7, p. 47]; light from an overcast sky (M) (curve I, Fig.4.3) [4.9]; north-sky light falling on a 45° plane (N) (curve II, Fig.4.3) [4.9]; and light from a clear, blue sky (H) [Ref.3.7, p. 47]

The color-temperature curve is a plot of the chromaticities that correspond to spectral distributions given by a precise equation of physics. A plot of the curve to 20,000 K and beyond to the theoretical limit of infinite temperature (indicated by the symbol ∞) is shown in Fig.7.15. Points (open circles) along the curve are labeled to show the color-temperature scale in kelvins. The chromaticities of the colors of the hole in the heated iron at 600 K, 1000 K, 1500 K, etc. are represented by the corresponding color-temperature points.

The chromaticity of the color of the sun, whose surface temperature is about 6000 K, is located at the point on the curve indicated by color temperature 6000 K, in the region of the chromaticity diagram that represents white light. EVANS described the white region as a "sausage-shaped" area that includes the color-temperature curve from about 4000 to 10,000 K [Ref.2.4, p. 51]. Although the length of the "sausage" is indicated, the only reference to its width is "the distance to either side of the color-temperature curve being shorter across than along it". The oval (dashed line) in Fig.7.1 is a guess for the shape of the region. At color temperatures that exceed 10,000 K, the corresponding chromaticities indicate colors of increasing saturation of bluish hues.

The color-temperature curve is of particular interest, because points that represent the chromaticities of the colors of light emitted by uncolored in-

Table 7.6. Chromaticity and color temperature. Several CIE illuminants and examples of daylight

	x	y	Color temperature [K]
CIE ILL A (typical of incandescent lamplight) [Ref.2.3, p. 166]	0.4476	0.4075	2850
CIE ILL B (typical of direct sunlight) [Ref.2.3, p. 166]	0.3484	0.3516	4874[a]
CIE ILL C (typical of average daylight) [Ref.2.3, p. 166]	0.3101	0.3162	6774[a]
CIE ILL D_{65} (typical of average daylight) [Ref.2.3, p. 166]	0.3127	0.3290	6504[a]
Direct sunlight [4.9]	0.3362	0.3502	5335
Light from overcast sky [4.9]	0.3134	0.3275	6500
Light from north sky on a 45° plane [4.9]	0.2773	0.2934	10,000
Light from equal-energy source E [Ref.2.3, p. 166]	0.3333	0.3333	5400[a]

[a]Correlated color temperature

candescent lamps and fluorescent lamps are located either on, or very close to, the curve (Fig.7.15). Thus, the chromaticity, in the case of a tungsten-filament incandescent lamp, given by the point (0.477, 0.414) can be expressed equally well by the color temperature 2500 K. If a chromaticity point is located close to the curve, a *correlated color temperature* is assigned to it [Ref.2.3, p. 167].

In Table 7.6 the chromaticity (x,y) and the color temperature or correlated color temperature are given for the equal-energy source E; CIE ILL A, B, C, and D_{65} (Figs.4.4 and 4.5); and the light from the sky under three conditions (for two, see curves I and II, Fig.4.3). The chromaticity point for a standard clear 60-watt tungsten-filament light bulb [Ref.2.3, p. 166] is approximately coincident with point A (CIE ILL A).

There are two advantages in using color temperatures and correlated color temperatures to represent chromaticities in specifications. The first is that only one number (for example 2500 K), instead of two (0.477, 0.414), is required. The second is that with a little experience we can visualize what 2500 K, 6000 K, or 12,000 K means in terms of perceived color.

8. Color Systems

8.1 CIE Color Space, CIE(x,y,Y)

It is often said that color is three dimensional. (This is true at least for psychophysical color and isolated psychological color.) But what is meant by the *three dimensions of color*? Commonly, we think of the word "dimensions" in terms of height, width, and depth, all stated in feet, meters, or other units of length. All objects have volume and occupy space; they are three dimensional.

The dimensions of color are the quantities that specify it. The dimensions of isolated psychological color are hue, saturation, and brightness. Those of psychophysical color are the CIE tristimulus values X, Y, and Z or three independent quantities derived from them such as x, y, and Y or the set λ_D, p_e, and Y or the set L, A, and B mentioned in Sect.8.2.

The chromaticity diagram, which is concerned with only x and y, is two dimensional; it can be accommodated on a flat piece of graph paper. However, in order to represent, simultaneously, the three dimensions x, y, and Y graphically, the points must be plotted in space — that is, CIE(x,y,Y) color space. Such color space can be visualized as containing a series of horizontal chro-

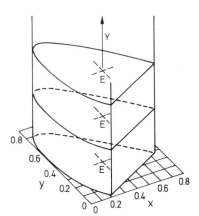

Fig. 8.1. CIE 1931 (x,y,Y) color space for light emitted by luminous objects

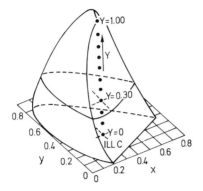

Fig. 8.2 CIE 1931 (x,y,Y) color space (defined by the MacAdam limits) for light scattered by or transmitted from nonfluorescent, non-self-luminous objects illuminated by light from a source typified by CIE ILL C. (Based on [Ref.3.7, Fig.3.22]; reprinted by permission of John Wiley & Sons, Inc., New York)

maticity diagrams arranged one precisely above another, like a series of floors in a high-rise building. Each chromaticity diagram in the series would accommodate points that represent colors of a single luminance Y. Thus, at one level, luminance Y would be 50, for example; at the next level above, 60; at the next, 70; etc. (Fig.8.1). We could, of course, imagine more-closely spaced levels, such as Y = 50, 51, 52, 53, etc., with a continuous variation of Y between the levels, permitting a color of Y = 52.6 to be located precisely. It should be noted that whereas only the chromaticity of a color is represented on a chromaticity diagramm (two dimensional), in Color space, color (psychophysical) itself is represented. (In the case of colored objects, the illuminant must also be known.)

If a beam of light A of one color (for which Y=50) is combined with a beam B of another color (for which Y=60), the resulting additive mixture M would have a luminance Y = 110. In CIE(x,y,Y) color space, the chromaticity point for the color of beam A would be at the level Y = 50, that of B would be at the level Y = 60, and that of M would be at Y = 110. The location of the chromaticity point for M at Y = 110 would be determined by the method explained in Sect.7.3.

CIE(x,y,Y) color space for the colors of *light* extends upward to a luminance level beyond which the light is dazzling and cannot be tolerated. On the other hand, CIE(x,y,Y) color space for the colors of nonluminous, nonfluorescent *objects* is defined by the MacAdam limits. In this case, we must imagine a structure more like a pyramid than a high-rise building. The floor plan at each level (according to the luminance factor Y) would have the shape outlined by the corresponding MacAdam limit. The floor plans at Y = 0, 0.10, 0.20,...1.00 are shown in Fig.7.8. The final pyramid has the form shown in Fig.8.2 in which one contour (or level) is indicated at Y = 0.30. Plate II

(color plate) shows samples of colors that are located at about the level of
Y = 0.30 in CIE(x,y,Y) color space. (This color space applies to situations
in which CIE ILL C characterizes the illumination.)

8.2 CIELAB Color Space

In Sect.7.9 the CIELAB(1976) system was mentioned in connection with the
measurement of color differences of nonluminous objects. The CIE tristimulus
values X, Y, and Z can be transformed by simple calculations to three quantities L, A, and B. These three quantities provide a different color space
of which the complete name is *CIELAB(1976) uniform color space*. It is also
called CIE 1976(L*a*b*) uniform color space [7.19]. The reason why CIELAB
color space is of great importance is that equal distances between colors in
any parts of CIELAB color space represent approximately equal perceptual differences; hence, it provides a useful measure for determining color differences numerically [7.21]. The formula used for calculating color differences
in terms of CIELAB units presents distances in CIELAB color space.

8.3 Color-Sample Systems

Although the CIE(x,y,Y) system for color specification is internationally
accepted and is in very active use, a number of systems that consist of *color
samples* are employed in applications for which less precision is demanded.
Some of these are used only in specific industries or trades (for example,
textile, building, plastics, and interior decorating); in certain cases, however, the samples are identified in terms of CIE(x,y,Y) specifications, which
makes them generally useful. Table 8.1 lists color systems that are, or could
be, of interest to artists and designers. Most of the systems provide printed
or painted samples. Other systems consist of light filters (liquids, plastics,
and glass). The table cites references that give further information about
the systems. The systems most familiar to artists and designers are the Munsell and Ostwald color systems, which are discussed in the next two sections.
The recently introduced OSA Uniform Color Scale samples, which are not intended for use in color specification, but which have other special utility
in art and design, are also considered in some detail.

The *DIN-Color Chart*, which bears certain similarity to the *Munsell Book
of Color* (Sect.8.4), is used extensively in color specification in Germany

Table 8.1. Color-sample systems and color atlases

1) *ARMY SOLUTIONS*. Colored solutions of chemicals. [Ref.4.10, p. 334; 8.1]

2) *COLOR ATLAS*, E.A. Hickethier. New York: Van Nostrand Reinhold, 1974. 1000 printed samples. Conversion to CIE(xyY).

3) *COLOR HARMONY MANUAL*, E. Jacobson, W.C. Granville, C.E. Foss. Chicago: Container Corporation of America, 1942, 1946, 1948 (3rd ed.). 949 paint samples on cellulose acetate. Matte and glossy sides. For use in design. See [8.2] for conversion to CIE(xyY). [Ref.2.3, p. 250; Ref.2.1, p. 165; Ref.6.1, p. 170; Ref.2.4, p. 167; 8.3-6]

4) *THE DICTIONARY OF COLOR*, A. Maerz and M.R. Paul. New York: McGraw-Hill, 1930, 1950. 7056 screen-plate printed samples on semi-glossy paper. For general use. For first edition see [8.2] for conversion to CIE(xyY). [Ref.2.3, p. 252; Ref.7.3, p. 11; Ref.2.1, p. 170; Ref.4.10, p. 337]

5) *DIN-FARBENKARTE* (Color Chart). Official Standard DIN-6164. Berlin: Beuth-Vertrieb, 1962. 585 matte paint chips. For general use. Conversion to CIE(xyY) and Munsell notation. [Ref.2.3, p. 266; Ref.3.7, p. 478; 8.7]

6) *FOSS COLOR-ORDER SYSTEM*, C.E. Foss. Pittsburgh: Graphic Arts Technical Foundation, 1972. 6000 different colors. For use in printing. [Ref.2.3, p. 254]

7) *HICKETHIER COLOR ATLAS*. (See *Color Atlas*)

8) *HORTICULTURAL COLOUR CHART*. The British Colour Council in collaboration with The Royal Horticultural Society (London). 1938, 1940. Copyright Robert F. Wilson. Printed samples. See [8.8] for conversion to Munsell notation.

9) *ICI COLOUR ATLAS*. Dyestuffs Division, Imperial Chemical Industries, Manchester, England. 1379 color samples and 19 gray filters (27,580 color possibilities). For use in textile industry. [8.9,10]

10) *LOVIBOND COLOR*. The Tintometer Ltd., Salisbury, England. Colored glass filters. 1900 color combinations. See [8.10a] for conversion to CIE(xyY). [Ref.2.3, p. 200]

11) *METHUEN HANDBOOK OF COLOUR*, 2nd edition, A. Kornerup and J.H. Wanscher. London: Methuen, 1963, 1967. 1266 printed samples (halftone). For general use. Conversion to Munsell notation. [8.11]

12) *MUNSELL BOOK OF COLOR*. Glossy and matte editions. Baltimore: Munsell Color Co., 1929,...1976. 1325 matte color chips; 1600 glossy color chips. For general use. See [8.12,13,14] for conversion to CIE(xyY). [2.3, p. 258; 2.1, p. 167; 3.7, p. 476; 6.1, p. 172; 4.10, p. 334; 2.4, p. 156; 8.3]

13) *NATURAL COLOUR SYSTEM ATLAS*. Stockholm: Svenskt Färgcentrum (Colour Centre). About 1400 painted chips. For architecture and design. Conversion to CIE(xyY). [2.3, p. 269; 8.15-19]

14) *NU-HUE CUSTOM COLOR SYSTEM* (1946). Martin-Senour Co., Chicago, Ill. 1000 painted cards. For use in the paint industry. Conversion to CIE(xyY) and Munsell notation. [2.3, p. 247; 2.1, p. 164; 8.1]

15) *OSA UNIFORM COLOR SCALES*. Optical Society of America, Washington, D.C. 558 glossy acrylic sample cards. For use in art and design. See [8.20] for conversion to CIE(xyY) and [8.21] for conversion to Munsell notation. [2.3, p. 270; 8.22,23]

16) *OSTWALD COLOR SYSTEM*. (See *Color Harmony Manual*)

Table 8.1 (continued)

---

17) *PLOCHERE COLOR SYSTEM*. Los Angeles: Fox Printing Co., 1948, 1965. 1248 color cards. For use in interior decorating. See [8.24] for conversion to Munsell notation. [7.3, p. 12]

18) *STANDARD COLOR CARD OF AMERICA*, 9th edition. New York: Color Association of the U.S.A., 1941. See [8.25] for conversion to CIE(xyY) and Munsell notation. [7.3, p. 13]

19) *VILLALOBOS COLOR ATLAS* (*Atlas de los Colores*). Buenos Aires: Libreria El Altenco Editorial, 1947. 7279 halftone prints. For general use. [2.1, p. 171]

20) *WILSON COLOUR CHART* (See *Horticultural Colour Chart*)

---

and in Central Europe. The DIN matte painted chips are classified by the three parameters DIN-Farbton (hue), DIN-Sättigung (saturation), and DIN-Dunkelstufe (relative lightness) [Ref.2.3, p. 266; Ref.5.3, p. 663]. The hue circle is divided into 24 perceptually equal steps and each hue is represented by a line of constant dominant wavelength (or complementary wavelength) with respect to CIE ILL C on the CIE chromaticity diagram. Each sample is identified by the DIN notation and also by CIE(x,y,Y) (CIE ILL C); CIE(λ_D,p_e,Y) (CIE ILL C); Munsell notations; and Ostwald notations.

8.4 The Munsell Color System

The most important color-sample system currently used in the U.S.A. is the Munsell color system (Sect.1.1). The Munsell notation has been incorporated in the Standards of the American National Standards Institute and the American Society for Testing Materials [8.12]. The Japanese color standards are based on the Munsell notation, and the British Standards Institute uses it in its designation of standard paints [1.11].

The Munsell color system offers two collections of standard painted samples: a matte-finish collection (about 1325 color chips) and a glossy-finish collection (about 1600 color chips). Both collections are increased from time to time, whenever more saturated pigments of acceptable permanence become available. The standard color samples appear in chip form in the *Munsell Book of Color* (two volumes) [1.22]. The samples are also available as cards in file boxes and as loose sheets. Inexpensive, small-sample student sets (matte finish), of less than standards quality, are available for color instruction.

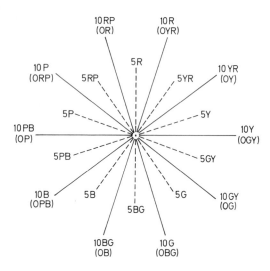

Fig. 8.3. The 10 Hue ranges of
the Munsell Hue circle

In the system, surface colors are identified by three quantities: *Munsell
Hue*, *Munsell Chroma*, and *Munsell Value*. They permit quantitative specification for surface colors under specified conditions of viewing: average daylight (CIE ILL C), 45° illumination, and viewing along a sight-line perpen-
dicular to the surface [Ref.7.3, p. 7]. A neutral gray background is usually
used when the color of a sample is identified by comparing it with Munsell
color chips. Specific recommendations are given in [Ref.7.3, p. 7] for variations of the technique for determining the colors of matte and glossy surfaces, satin-finished textiles, liquids, glasses, fluorescent materials,
microscopic specimens, etc.

There are 10 Hue ranges in the Hue circle of the Munsell system, which
appear in the order (clockwise)(Fig.8.3): R (red), YR (yellow-red), Y (yellow), GY (green-yellow), G (green), BG (blue-green), B (blue), PB (purple-
blue), P (purple), and RP (red-purple). The Hue circle is subdivided by a
scale consisting of 100 equally spaced Hue radii. A Hue range (for example R)
includes eleven Hue radii, 0-10; the terminal Hue radius 10 of one range coincides with the initial Hue radius 0 of the next range. For each Hue range,
there is a major Hue, which is located at the middle of each Hue range —
that is, along Hue radius 5. The major Hues are designated 5R, 5YR, 5Y, 5GY,
and so on. The Hues along the terminal radii of the ranges are designated
10R, 10YR, 10Y, 10GY,.... Fig.8.3 shows the radii for the major Hues (dashed
lines) and the radii for the terminal Hues (solid lines). The numbering of
the radii progresses clockwise from 0 to 10 in each range. Because the Hue

along each terminal radius is identical with the Hue at the beginning of the
next range, Hue 10R, for example is identical with Hue 0YR. But the designation 0YR is not customarily used. This is similar to the hour of the day
given in schedules for train and air travel. The end of the day, midnight,
is given by 24:00. That moment may also be given by 0:00, the beginning of
the next day, but the designation 0:00 is not used. But three minutes after
midnight is indicated 0:03, and similarly on the Munsell Hue circle a Hue
that is a bit more yellow than 10R might be, for example, 0.2YR.

Munsell color chips are provided not only for Hues at radii 5 and 10 in
each of the ten Hue ranges but also for Hues at intermediate radii 2.5 and
7.5. Thus, the collection of the chips provides for a total of forty Hues:
2.5R, 5R, 7.5R, 10R; 2.5YR, 5YR, 7.5YR, 10YR; 2.5Y, 5Y, 7.5Y, 10Y; and so on
for the seven remaining Hue ranges. The equal angular spacing (9°) of the
forty Hue radii is meaningful, because the Hues have been selected to be perceptually equally spaced.

Munsell Value is designated on a scale from 0 to 10. The Munsell Value of
a color is an indicator of the lightness of perceived color. Munsell Value
is calculated from the luminous reflectance (luminance factor) measured for
a sample [Ref.2.4, p. 157].

Munsell Chroma is often considered to be the approximate counterpart of
perceived saturation. The Munsell Chroma of a color sample is defined as the
difference from a gray of the same lightness. The Chroma scale is measured
along a Hue radius; Chroma is zero at the center (neutral gray) and increases outward in uniform steps to a maximum Chroma at the MacAdam limit determined for each Hue and Value. (The maximum Chromas are tabulated in [8.26].)
Munsell color samples are offered at Chromas 1, 2, 4, 6, 8, ... up to the
maximum producible with pigments of acceptable permanency for each of the
forty Hues. The uniform steps of Chroma from 2 to 4, 4 to 6, 6 to 8, etc.,
are intended to represent equal perceptual steps.

Figure 8.4 shows the major Hue radii, the terminal Hue radii, and concen-
tric Chroma circles that represent equal Chroma steps. The diagram shows with
dots all colors at Value 5 for which glossy Munsell samples are presently
available. The central point, which represents zero Chroma, represents a neutral gray sample. Glossy color chips that have Chromas as high as 16 are
available for reds R and yellow-reds YR.

Section 6.4 mentioned that dominant wavelength and purity are not precise
indicators of perceived hue and saturation. JUDD wrote, "...Munsell hue, value, and chroma reflect the psychological facts of object color to a good

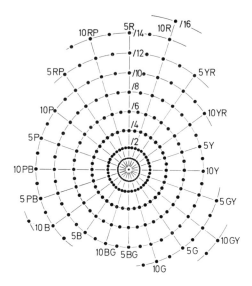

Fig. 8.4. Available Munsell standard color samples (indicated by dots). Reported are 40 Hues and Chromas up to 16 at Munsell Value 5 (luminance factor
Y=0.20). Hue radii are not shown for the intermediate Hues 2.5R, 7.5R, 2.5YR,
7.5YR, etc.

approximation, whereas dominant wavelength, luminous directional reflectance,
and excitation purity reflect them only to a poor approximation" [Ref.6.4,
p. 852].

It should be noted that, although the Munsell color system offers uniform
perceptual measures of Hue, Value, and Chroma, the units of one are not equal
to those of another. This is shown by the following: 1 Value unit equals 10
NBS units (Sect.7.9); 1 Chroma unit equals 7 NBS units; 1 Hue unit equals
0.4 NBS units at Chroma 1 [Ref.2.3, p. 317]. A Hue unit is taken as 1/100th
of the Hue circle (or 1/10th of a Hue range). Alternatively, 1 Value unit is
equivalent to about 1.5 Chroma units and to 25 Hue units at Chroma 1 (or to
3 Hue units at Chroma 5 [Ref.6.1, p. 175]).

Plate V (color plate) shows dots that represent presently available Munsell glossy chips of maximum Chroma for forty Hues at Value 6. The heavy line
drawn through the dots encloses the full gamut of available Munsell glossy
samples at Value 6. The line is reproduced in Fig.8.5 on a reduced scale to
enable comparison of the gamut with the larger gamut theoretically possible
(MacAdam limit) at Value 6. A great difference is indicated between the present maximum (Chroma 10) for glossy chips of Hue 5G and the limiting Chroma

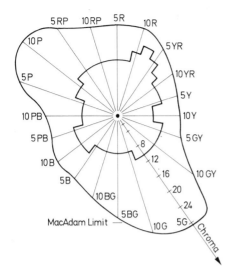

Fig. 8.5. Gamut of available Munsell standard color samples reproduced on a smaller scale from Plate V for comparison with the MacAdam limit at Munsell Value 6 (luminance factor Y=0.30) (CIE ILL C)

28. Perhaps this difference will be decreased somewhat by the introduction of new stable pigments.

Also represented in Plate V are the Munsell samples and the commercial color samples displayed in Plate II. The colors of the samples have a Munsell Value of 6 (Y=0.30), approximately. Two of the commercial samples fall outside of the gamut of the Munsell samples.

The painted chips in the *Munsell Book of Color* are grouped so that only one Munsell Hue, say 5YR, is represented on a page, and the chips are arranged to display variations in Munsell Value and Munsell Chroma. The dots shown in Fig.8.6 represent available glossy chips for Hues 5YR and 5B, arranged so that Chroma increases radially (horizontally) from the vertical *neutral axis*. The neutral grays are represented on the neutral axis over the range from Value 0 (black) to Value 10 (white). For Hue 5YR and Chroma 4, for example, seven chips are indicated that vary in lightness from Value 2 up to Value 8.

Also shown in Fig.8.6 are the MacAdam limits for Hues 5YR and 5B [8.26]. In the case of yellow-red YR, chips are available up to Chroma 14, which approach the MacAdam limit rather closely. In the case of blue 5B, there is a greater gap between what is available in Munsell chips and what is theoretically possible.

Figure 8.7 shows two disks, one directly above the other in space. We can imagine such disks at equally spaced levels, represented by Values 1 to 9; each disk contains a circular array of points or dots, such as those shown in Fig.8.4. Then, if the imagined disks are made to disappear, the arrays of

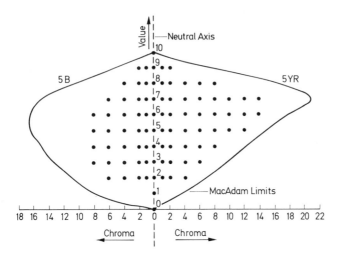

Fig. 8.6. Gamut of available Munsell standard color samples for complementary Hues 5B and 5YR for comparison with the corresponding MacAdam limits (CIE ILL C)

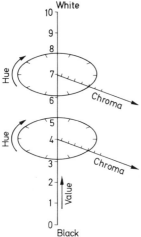

Fig. 8.7. Cylindrical arrangement of Hue, Chroma, and Value in Munsell color space

dots remain in space, flat clouds of dots in *Munsell color space*. Each dot represents a different Munsell color (there are about 1600 glossy color chips!). The part of Munsell color space occupied by all of the clouds of dots has the form, roughly, of an onion; this portion of color space is called the *Munsell color solid*. Munsell color space, on the other hand, is bounded by the MacAdam limits; it has, let us say, the form of a turnip. (A

Table 8.2. Conversion table. Munsell Value V
and luminance factor Y (reflectance) or transmittance [8.13]

V	Y	V	Y
0.00	0.0000	6.00	0.300
0.85	0.0100	6.16	0.320
1.00	0.0121	6.33	0.340
1.49	0.0200	6.48	0.360
1.50	0.0202	6.50	0.362
1.95	0.0300	6.64	0.380
2.00	0.0313	6.78	0.400
2.31	0.0400	7.00	0.431
2.50	0.0461	7.06	0.440
2.61	0.0500	7.33	0.480
2.87	0.0600	7.50	0.507
3.00	0.0656	7.58	0.520
3.10	0.0700	7.82	0.560
3.31	0.0800	8.00	0.591
3.50	0.0900	8.05	0.600
3.68	0.100	8.27	0.640
4.00	0.120	8.48	0.680
4.29	0.140	8.50	0.684
4.50	0.156	8.68	0.720
4.55	0.160	8.87	0.760
4.80	0.180	9.00	0.787
5.00	0.198	9.06	0.800
5.03	0.200	9.24	0.840
5.24	0.220	9.41	0.880
5.44	0.240	9.50	0.900
5.50	0.246	9.66	0.940
5.64	0.260	9.82	0.980
5.82	0.280	9.90	1.000
		10.00	1.026

model of the latter space is shown in [8.26].) We can therefore imagine the
color solid within color space as an onion positioned within the shell of a
large turnip. A vertical cross section of such a combination is shown in
Fig.8.6 where the MacAdam limits provide a profile of the turnip and the dots
suggest the onion (deformed!). Similarly, a horizontal cross section is shown
in Fig.8.5.

The Munsell notation is easily described by an example: a yellow chip,
designated by Hue 7.5Y, Value 7, and Chroma 8. In Munsell notation, the Chroma is written /8 (Fig.8.4), and the color is designated 7.5Y 7/8. The neutral
grays are indicated by the letter N in place of the Hue designation. Because
they have zero Chroma, Chroma is not indicated. Thus a neutral gray of Value
6 is designated simply by N 6/.

Color specifications given as CIE(x,y,Y), CIE ILL C, can be converted to
Munsell notation by use of a table and a set of nine charts published in

[8.13] and in [3.7]. The table, which permits conversions between Munsell Value and luminance factor Y, is presented in abbreviated form as Table 8.2 of this book. Conversions to Munsell notations usually require fractional numbers for Hue, Value, and Chroma. For example, a designation might be 8.4Y 7.36/8.9.

The 1929 edition of the *Munsell Book of Color* was for many years the authoritative source for Munsell notation. Notations determined with its use were called *Munsell Book notations* [Ref.7.3, p. A-1]. In a report published in 1943, a committee of the Optical Society of America improved the spacing of the samples and extended the Munsell notation to the MacAdam limits [8.13]. For some years, colors brought into conformity with the 1943 report were specified by what was called *Munsell renotations*. Now that a sufficient number of years have passed, so that there need be no confusion with the old Munsell Book notations, the term *Munsell notation* is now used for new chips. The current editions of the *Munsell Book of Color* conform fully with the 1943 report.

This section should not close without a brief mention of two matters concerned with color perception. Formerly, uniform steps of Value in the *Munsell Book of Color* were established by visual means, just as those in Hue and in Chroma continue to be. But because observers often fail to agree in comparing the lightness of samples at high Chroma the OSA committee decided, arbitrarily, to define Value in relation to luminance factor by use of a mathematical formula (cf. Table 8.2) [Ref.2.4, p. 166].

Another comment concerns Chroma directly. It was mentioned earlier that Munsell Chroma is usually considered to be the approximate counterpart of perceived saturation. Until recently, this notion was, it seems, not questioned. But now qualification of this concept must be considered, because EVANS' experimental work showed that saturation and brilliance are both combined in the perception of Chroma [Ref.2.4, p. 168].

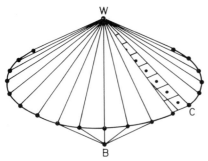

Fig. 8.8. Ostwald color solid

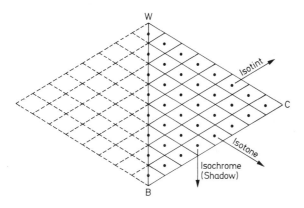

Fig. 8.9. Vertical cross section of the Ostwald color solid

8.5 The Ostwald Color System

In the *Ostwald color system*, the color solid is a double cone — that is, two
identical cones that have a common base with the central axis oriented ver-
tically. In Fig.8.8, the double cone is shown with one slice (sector) removed. There are 24 equal slices in the double cone; each slice represents
one hue and is triangular. Two triangles of complementary color gamuts (which
appear as opposite slices in the color solid) are shown in Fig.8.9. The vertical edges of all of the 24 triangles are joined to form the white-black
axis; it is the vertical central axis of the double cone; it extends from
the south pole B (black) to the north pole W (white). Points along the axis
represent neutral grays that vary by progressive steps from black to white
[8.6].

Chemist Wilhelm Ostwald (1853-1932), the originator of the system, considered that all colors of surfaces viewed under nonisolated conditions —
that is, related colors — are mixtures of hypothetical *full colors* (surface
colors of maximum possible freedom from perceived blackness and whiteness
[Ref.2.4, p. 167]) with black and white [8.4]. The apex of the triangle (point
C) represents the full color of a given hue; all other points within the triangle represent mixtures of the full color with black and white [8.3]. At
each point, definite percentages of the full color, black, and white are assigned; those assignments are identical for all 24 hues. The color mixtures
are produced by color mixture by averaging when those percentages of the area
of a rotating disk are occupied by sectors of the full color, black, and
white (Sect.5.8).

The points along the line that connects W to C represent mixtures of white and full color C. The lines of mixture points parallel to the line connecting W to C are called *isotone lines*. Along each isotone line, the colors represented contain a fixed proportion of black. Points along the line that connects B to C represent mixtures of black and the full color. Lines parallel to this line are called *isotint lines*; each such line corresponds to colors that contain a fixed proportion of white. Vertical lines through the points are called *isochrome lines*, because they represent colors of the same chromaticity and hue; but their luminance factors vary. *Isovalent loci* are circles in horizontal planes that pass through the Ostwald double cone; they connect points for colors that have the same black and white contents but different hues. The equator of the color solid is an isovalent locus that passes through the equally spaced full-color points C for the 24 hues.

Certain problems have been encountered in applying the Ostwald color system [8.3,5]. However, a practical modification was devised and presented in the *Color Harmony Manual* [1.20,8.6]. One purpose for the *Manual* was "to promote the knowledge and study of color harmony and color coordination in design" [Ref.2.3, p. 251]. Originally, the *Manual* contained 24 charts of hue triangles. In the third edition (the *Manual* is no longer published), the number was increased to 30; it contains 943 matte and glossy color samples. In the *Manual*, each color triangle presents a gamut that contains 28 colors of one dominant wavelength; each triangle is paired with the opposite triangle in the double cone (Fig.8.9); the latter contains colors of the complementary hue (dominant wavelength). The colors C are pigment approximations to the Ostwald full colors.

The *Manual* has been of interest to artists, because the isotint and isotone series of lines offer rather good approximations to the color gradations observed in nature. An isochrome series (usually called a shadow series) simulates the perception of different levels of light and shade [Ref.6.1, p. 171]. Thus, the shaded greens of a vertical green pole illuminated from one side may be represented in a painting by an isochrome series of greens.

8.6 The Natural Colour System (NCS)

The *Natural Colour System* provides an effective means for everyone with normal color vision to make color evaluations without the use of color-measuring instruments or of color samples for comparison. The NCS can be employed directly for determining the color of a wall in a room, of foliage in the distance, of a painted area in which simultaneous contrast occurs, of a spot on a television screen, etc. A color determined in this way is an absolute measurement based on color perception. It differs from psychophysical determinations, which rely on color matching.

The conception of the NCS has been traced to the German physiologist Ewald Hering (1834-1918) whose theory of color vision continues to receive growing support. The NCS was revived by the Swedish physicist Tryggve Johansson (1905-1960), and research concerned with it has been pursued at the Swedish Colour Centre Foundation at Stockholm [8.15,18].

Basic to the NCS is the recognition of the six *psychological primaries* (Sect.3.2): white, black, yellow, red, blue, and green. The last four are the unitary hues: yellow that is neither greenish nor reddish, red that is neither yellowish nor bluish, blue that is neither reddish nor greenish, and green that is neither bluish nor yellowish [Ref.2.4, pp. 66,107]. All other hues are recognized as mixtures of two unitary hues; for example, greenish yellows, reddish yellows, yellowish reds, bluish reds.

The first step in judging a color by the NCS is determination of the hue [8.15,17,18]. Plate VI (color plate) shows the hue circle attributed to HERING [8.15]. The hue circle is also shown below, stretched out into a straight band. The unitary hues, indicated by Y, R, G, and B, are at equally spaced locations on the circle. The pure, unmixed character of each is represented by the one color at its location on the color band. For example, at position R, the color band is red only. Except at Y, R, G, and B, all hues are represented as mixtures of two components. The dashed lines indicate hues of 50/50 mixtures: YR, RB, BG, and GY. The dashed lines also indicate hue ranges. Thus the yellows extend from GY to YR. The yellows between GY and Y have green in them; they are greenish. The yellows between Y and YR are reddish. In this terminology, common hue terms, such as orange, purple, and cyan are deliberately avoided. But, of course, browns and olives must be recognized in place of yellows and yellowish greens when the luminance factor is low (for the colors of nonluminous objects). The unitary hues that are opposite to each other on the hue circle do not, in the NCS and in the Hering theory, combine to form new hues. Otherwise, we would be able to experience greenish reds, reddish greens, bluish yellows, and yellowish blues [Ref.8.18, p. 111].

To judge hue, the observer must first identify the two unitary hues between which the hue is located. When this is done, then the observer judges the relative proportions of the two unitary hues required to produce the hue. For example, the observer may decide that the hue is located between G and Y. Imagine that, after some consideration, the hue is judged to be 30% unitary

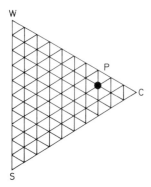

Fig. 8.10. NCS graphical representation of relative amounts of white (W), black (S), and
chromatic component (C) in a perceived color
(P)

green and 70% unitary yellow. Because more than 50% of the hue is unitary
yellow, the hue would be said to be yellow with 30% green (a greenish yellow).
Thus, in NCS notation, the hue is designated Y30G. If, on the other hand, the
hue is a green, a yellowish green, such that the proportions are 20% yellow
and 80% green, the NCS hue designation would be G20Y. If the hue is 50% green
and 50% yellow, then the hue is designated by GY.

The next task is to judge, by inspection, the relative amounts of chromatic
component C [for example, greenish yellow (hue Y30G)], and achromatic components white W and black S. Let us say that after inspection the judge decides
that the relative amounts are: S, 10%; W, 20%; and C, 70%. Now, all of the
information is available for the NCS specification of the color. It is: 1070
Y30G, where the relative amount of black S (10%) is listed first, that of the
chromatic component C (70%) second, and finally the hue (Y30G). Only two of
the relative amounts are stated, because the third, white W, can be obtained
by subtracting the sum of S and C from 100.

The relative amounts of S, W, and C are commonly represented by a point
on a triangular diagram (Fig.8.10), which is similar to the triangle obtained
by taking a slice from the Ostwald solid (Fig.8.9). The result just described
is represented by P. The method for locating a point on an equal-sided triangular diagram is explained in Sect.6.2.

At the Swedish Colour Centre Foundation, extensive tests on the application of the NCS have shown that people with no particular knowledge about
color and with no previous experience in color specification or in color measurement are capable of making the aforementioned judgments of hue, C, W,
and S, unaided by color samples [Ref.8.18, p. 116]. A *Colour Atlas* containing
about 1400 samples is being produced at the Foundation [1.21;8.16,18]. Although the *Atlas* is not required for making NCS color judgments, it will be

useful for precise specification of colors on the basis of perceptual criteria. In this sense, it will resemble the *Munsell Book of Color*. The NCS and the Munsell system represent different samplings of essentially the same color space; probably a simple relationship exists between them [8.19]. The *Atlas* samples will also be identified by CIE(x,y,Y) for universal reference.

The *Atlas* collection of color samples will comprise a NCS color solid, basically of the form of the Ostwald system (*Color Harmony Manual*) (Fig.8.8). There is, however, a major difference in the quantities represented on the triangles, the slices from the color solid. In the Ostwald triangles, the relative amounts of black, white, and full color are indicated, for the production of color by color mixture by averaging. On the other hand, in the NCS triangles the relative amounts are judgments of perceptions. This is probably of significance to artists interested in the use of the shadow series and of the isotone and isotint series in their work (Fig.8.9). Undoubtedly, the NCS *Atlas* will find many practical applications and will replace the Ostwald color system in certain areas in art and design.

8.7 The OSA Uniform Color Scales

The Committee on Uniform Color Scales of the Optical Society of America (OSA) has made available a collection of glossy acrylic paint color cards (5 × 5 cm) of 558 colors of which 424 comprise a unique set that is of particular interest in art and design [8.22,23,27,28]. For each color in the set of 424 there are 12 neighbor colors that differ from it by the *same perceptual amount*. (There are less than 12 neighbor colors for those few at the limit of the gamut.) In OSA Committee color space, the gamut of these colors is represented by a spatial arrangement of points, and *any* chosen point within the arrangement is surrounded by 12 nearest-neighbor points, all at an equal distance from the chosen point. The objective of the OSA Committee project was the "provision of a set of colors with which the maximum number and variety of uniform color scales can be constructed" [8.27]. The set is intended "for study and use by artists and designers, as well as by scientists" [8.23].

A *uniform color scale* is a sequence of color samples that differ by equal perceptual amounts. Three hundred and ninety-eight uniform color scales can be selected from the set of 424 cards [8.28]. The number of colors in each uniform color scale varies from three to nine. (Thirty-six of the scales possess only three colors.) Only about fifty scales include a neutral gray and complementary colors. (Colors that are complementary in OSA Committee color

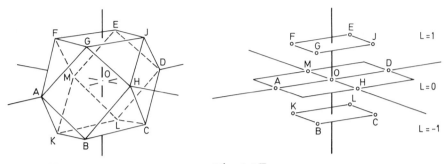

Fig. 8.11   Fig. 8.12

Fig. 8.11. Cubo-octahedron showing locations of 12 equidistant nearest-neigh-bor points around a central point

Fig. 8.12. The 12 equidistant points (see Fig.8.11) lie on square grids in horizontal planes

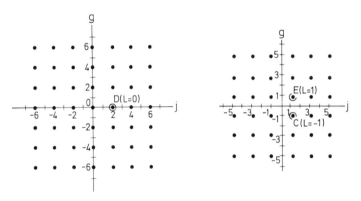

Fig. 8.13   Fig. 8.14

Fig. 8.13. Square-grid arrangement of points in even-numbered horizontal planes (L=0,2,4,6,...; L=-2,-4,-6,...)

Fig. 8.14. Square-grid arrangement of points in odd-numbered horizontal planes (L=1,3,5,...; L=-1,-3,-5,...)

space are generally nearly complementary by the CIE measure discussed in Sect.7.2). Most of the color scales have probably never been seen before; hence, they are very interesting.

In order to select samples from the set to construct uniform color scales and color charts, it is necessary to be familiar with the structure of OSA Committee color space. An idea of the structure can be gained by considering a symmetrical cluster of 13 color sample points in the color space: one color sample point surrounded by 12 nearest-neighbor points all at equal distance.

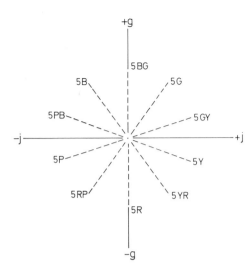

Fig. 8.15. A horizontal plane (j,g). Hue regions are indicated approximately by the superimposed Munsell major Hue radii (dashed lines)

The arrangement of the 13 points in OSA Committee color space corresponds precisely to the points locating the 12 corners and the center of the geometrical form shown in Fig.8.11 [8.29]. The form is called a cubo-octahedron; it may be constructed by merely cutting off the eight corners of a cube. The cuts are made to leave eight equal triangular faces with each vertex of each triangle touching a vertex of another. Between the triangular faces are six square faces, the remnants of the faces of the original cube.

It is important first to consider that each of the 12 points that surround point 0 has its set of 12 nearest-neighbor equidistant points and that this pattern continues throughout OSA Committee color space. For example, point J has as its nearest neighbors points D, E, G, H, 0, and seven other points (not shown). The second important feature is that all 13 points can fall on square grids in horizontal planes (Fig.8.12).

In OSA Committee color space all sample points are located on square grids on equally separated horizontal planes. Fig.8.12 shows the arrangement of the points at grid intersections on the horizontal planes, called lightness levels [8.27]. Lightness levels start at the central horizontal plane (L=0) and are numbered upward L = 1, 2, 3, ... and downward L = -1, -2, -3, ... The two quantities required to locate a point on the grid of any lightness level are given by j and g (Figs.8.13 and 8.14).

It is clear in Fig.8.12 that, although points E, F, G, and J that define one square unit are located directly above points L, K, B, and C, they are displaced by a half-grid unit length with respect to points such as A, 0, and H, which define square-grid units of the same size on the horizontal plane in between. The points in alternate horizontal planes of even number (L=0; L=2,4,6,...; L=-2,-4,-6,...) are located at even-numbered intersections (Fig. 8.13). Thus, point O of the cubo-octahedron can be located at $j = 0$, $g = 0$ and point D at $j = 2$, $g = 0$, each at lightness level L = 0. On the other hand, the points in uneven-numbered planes (L=1,3,5,...; L=-1,-3,-5,...) are located at uneven-numbered intersections (Fig.8.14). Thus point E (L=1) is at $j = 1$ and $g = 1$, and point C (L=-1) is at $j = 1$ and $g = -1$.

We can now turn our attention to the colors represented at points in OSA Committee color space — that is, points given by L, j, and g. The neutral-gray samples are located at $j = 0$, $g = 0$ at lightness levels L = 0, 2, 4, ... and L = -2, -4, ... They become lighter with increasing L. At L = 0, the central lightness plane, the gray is a medium gray that has luminance factor Y = 0.30 (Munsell Value 6). The grays are given in equal perceptual steps, but they are not nearest neighbors, because they are represented only on alternate (even-numbered) lightness levels. (Samples that have equal L do not have equal Y or Munsell Value [8.20,23,27].)

All of the colors of the set of samples, which are limited to pigments of great permanency, are represented on lightness levels between L = 5 (Munsell Value 8.7 on the neutral axis, $j\leqfq0$, g=0) and L = -7 (Munsell Value 2.3 on the neutral axis), the lightness limits of the set [8.23,30]. Fig.8.15 shows the radii of the Munsell major Hues (Sect.8.4) arranged in counterclockwise order and superimposed on the central lightness plane L = 0. The radii give an approximate idea of the hues expected in regions on a lightness plane. The equal perceptual spacing characteristic of the set applies to conditions of a 10° visual angle, a neutral-gray background, and illumination typified by CIE ILL D_{65} (Sect.6.3) [8.27].

By referring to the cubo-octahedron, we can see that a maximum of six straight lines can be passed through any point and two opposite nearest points. If one such line is extended in both directions from any point that represents a color sample in OSA Committee color space to the limits of the gamut of the sample colors, it will pass through points that represent a set of uniformly spaced colors. This is a uniform color scale. Each color sample is on six such scales.

We can also pass cleavage planes through the points of OSA Committee color space to produce a variety of color arrays [8.23]. Such an array of colors can be presented usefully on a color chart. Horizontal cleavage planes produce uniform color arrays of samples of constant lightness over 13 levels from lightness L = 5 to the darkest L = -7. In each case, a chart would show a square-grid array having rows in which j is varied, and columns in which g is varied [Ref.8.23, Table 1].

Many vertical cleavage planes can be passed through points in OSA Committee color space to provide interesting rectangular-grid arrays of colors. Vertical planes passed through the neutral-gray axis — that is, through $j = 0$, $g = 0$ at all levels L — produce arrays of samples in essentially two hues (two sets of complementary colors separated by neutral-gray samples). Only two of these complementary-color vertical planes (one that passes through point j=2, g=2 and the other through point j=-2, g=2) pass through arrays of equally spaced points at the closest-neighbor distance. These points lie along diagonals on the planes and determine square grids. In one of these two vertical cleavage planes, the arrays of complementary colors are of a green and a purple hue; in the other plane, they are of a blue and an orange hue. Of course, other vertical planes with square-grid arrays of equally spaced points can be constructed parallel to these two planes, but they will not contain neutral grays and will not display arrays of complementary colors (two hues).

Four triangular-grid arrays of equally spaced colors can be obtained by passing four oblique cleavage planes through point $j = 0$, $g = 0$ at level $L = 0$. One plane passes through $j = 2$, and the second through $j = -2$, both at $L = 2$ and all values of g; the third plane passes through $g = 2$ and the last through $g = -2$, both at $L = 2$ and all values of j. More arrays of equally spaced colors are found by constructing sets of planes parallel to these four planes.

Tabulations that identify in Munsell terms the colors in three representative equally spaced arrays (horizontal plane, vertical plane, and oblique plane) are presented by NICKERSON in [8.23]. The Munsell notations for the colors of all the OSA-UCS samples are given by the same author in [8.21]. Tabulations of the notations in $CIE(x_{10}, y_{10}, Y_{10})$ and in $CIE(x,y,Y)$ are given in [8.20].

8.8 ISCC-NBS Color Names of Materials

It is estimated that a normal eye can distinguish about 10 million different colors and that in ordinary commerce about a half million different colors are recognized [Ref.2.3, p. 388]. These facts show the need for a precise numerical system for color specification, such as $CIE(x,y,Y)$. In many instances, however, great precision is not necessary and several hundred color names will suffice. For such purposes, in the U.S.A. an official list of 267

standardized color names that apply to the colors of nonluminous materials
has been presented jointly by the Inter-Society Color Council and the National
Bureau of Standards (ISCC-NBS) [7.3].

In 1933, the ISCC undertook to devise a means to designate color for pharmaceutical use yet "sufficiently standardized as to be acceptable and usable
by science, sufficiently broad to be appreciated and used by science, art and
industry, and sufficiently commonplace to be understood, at least in a general way, by the whole public" [Ref.7.3, p. 1]. A system of color names was
devised; it was revised in 1955. The present list of *ISCC-NBS color names* is
given in Table 8.3. The listed names apply to opaque materials, but they can
be extended to include light-transmitting materials by substituting "colorless" for "white", "faint pink" for "pinkish white", "faint yellow" for "yellowish white", etc., as shown in Table 8.3. The color names are numbered;
these numbers, called *centroid numbers*, may also be used to designate a color.

In order to be able to assign an ISCC-NBS color name or color centroid
number to a color, the color's specification must first be known in terms of
Munsell Hue, Value, and Chroma. With the specification, the name and number
can then be determined by consulting either the set of 31 color-name charts
published in *Color: Universal Language and Dictionary of Names* [7.3] or Tables
8.3 and 8.4 of this book, which present in tabular form the information presented in graphical form in those charts.

The ISCC-NBS color names and centroid numbers refer to well-defined colorname blocks or zones that fill the region of Munsell color space that includes most commonly experienced surface colors. Each color-name block defines a restricted range of colors that can be represented by a common name.
The forms of the individual blocks and their locations in color space can be
determined readily from the charts. In another publication [8.31], the National Bureau of Standards offers a set of color samples whose specifications
correspond to the central points of the color-name blocks in Munsell color
space. This sample set is displayed on the *ISCC-NBS Centroid Color Charts*.

To use the set of 31 charts in [7.3], the point that represents the Munsell specification is located in color space and the color-name block that
encloses the point is noted. The procedure is simple and quick.

Table 8.4 provides an alternative, more compact in presentation. Here,
again, the block that includes the point must be found. Before considering
an example, note the arrangement of Table 8.4. The first column (at the left)
presents the Value range for each of the blocks. The second column gives the
particular numerical values of Chroma (0, 0.5, 0.7, 1, 1.2, ..., 40) that are
used to designate the Chroma range of the blocks. The third column gives the

particular Munsell Hues (9RP, 1R, 4R, ...) that designate the Hue range of
the blocks. The last column gives the centroid numbers. Some centroid numbers
appear two or three times in the last column. The reason is that, in those
cases, the blocks are irregular. To simplify Table 8.4, they have been cut
into two or three pieces that have forms (six-faced) that can be described
by one set of three ranges. Another simplification employed is use of the
upper Value limit 10, the lower Value limit 0, or the upper Chroma limit 40
[Ref.8.26, Table I] where a definite Value or Chroma boundary for a color
block at the limit of the color gamut is not indicated in the ISCC-NBS color-name charts.

To illustrate the procedure for using Table 8.4, let us consider a color
for which the Munsell designation is 5R 7/4. There are several steps:

1) Consult the pages of Table 8.4 on which the Hue in question is included.
Hue 5R is included within the ranges shown on pp. 110 and 111.

2) Note the tabulated ranges of Value that include the Value of interest.
For Value 7, the following ranges must be considered on p.110: 6.5-10, 6.5-
8.5, 6.5-8.0, and 6.5-7.5. On p.111 there is one additional range: 4.5-10.

3) In parts of the table where the ranges of Value are considered, simultaneously trace downward between the two consecutive columns of Chroma (i.e.,
Chroma 3 and 5) that bracket the Chroma of interest (Chroma 4) and between
the two columns of Hue (i.e., Hues 4R and 6R) that bracket the Hue of interest (Hue 5R). On the horizontal line on which *both* Chroma 4 and Hue 5R are
bracketed by 0's, the last column gives the centroid number sought: 5. The
color name is then found by consulting Table 8.3. For centroid number 5, the
color is shown to be "moderate pink".

Colors that are slightly different are often found to be in the same color-
name block in Munsell color space; hence, they share the same ISCC-NBS color
name and centroid number. For example, color samples I-A and I-B in Plate IV
(color plate) have the same color names; samples I-E and I-F also have the
same color name (Table 7.5).

Sometimes, in Munsell color space, the location of a color is on a boundary between two color-name blocks. In this case, two ISCC-NBS color names
clearly apply. Cases may be found in which as many as eight color names apply, as for the color whose Munsell notation is 7Y 8/8. Here, the location
of the color in Munsell color space is at a point where the corners of eight
color-name blocks touch.

To avoid the ambiguity of multiple color names, it seems generally preferable to alter very slightly, but in a consistent way, all quantities in a
Munsell notation that lead to more than one color name. I suggest that Value

be increased by 0.1 if its amount if given by one of the following numbers:
1.5, 2.0, 2.5, 3.0, 3.5, 4.5, 5.5, 6.5, 7.5, 8.0, and 8.5. Thus if 7.5 is
given for the Value, then it would be taken as 7.6 for the purpose of determining a single color name. Similarly, if a Chroma or a Hue is numerically
identical to one appearing at the heads of columns in Table 8.4, then it would
be increased by 0.1 to avoid finding more than one color name. Thus Chroma 9
is raised to 9.1 for sample 6-B in Table 7.4, leading to the color name
"strong blue" (178). Similarly Hue 5PB is changed to 5.1PB, and the color
name for sample 6-C is found to be "light purplish blue" (199).

The ISCC-NBS color names have been adopted by *Webster's Third New International Dictionary* (Unabridged) [8.32]. But a color name can be assigned with
certainty only if the Munsell specification is known. If a color specification is given in CIE(x,y,Y), conversion to the specification in Munsell notation can be made by use of a set of charts and a table in [3.7,8.13]. In
Table 8.1, several color-sample systems are indicated (for example, the Swedish *Natural Colour System Atlas*, the *Color Atlas* of Hickethier, and the West
German *DIN-6164*) that include conversions from their notations to the Munsell
notation or to CIE(x,y,Y). In some systems in which such conversions are not
included, references are cited in Table 8.1 that tell where the needed conversions may be found.

In some color-sample systems, color names such as "bambino", "Bavarian
blue" and "Hooker's green" are given to specific color samples. If a color-
sample system is one of the 14 listed in [Ref.7.3, p. 14], the ISCC-NBS color
name and centroid number corresponding to the system's color name given to
a sample (e.g., "Bavarian blue") can be found by consulting the Dictionary
of Color Names [Ref.7.3, pp. 85-158] wherein 7500 terms are listed. Also indicated in each case is the color-sample system that employs the name. Thus,
for "Bavarian blue", the corresponding ISCC-NBS color name is "dark blue",
the centroid number is 183 and the source is the Plochere Color System (interior decoration) (Table 8.1). For "Hooker's green", [7.3] indicates that
it is included in the color system of Maerz and Paul [*Dictionary of Color*
(Table 8.1)] and that two color samples are assigned that name: "Hooker's
green No.1" for which the ISCC-NBS color name and centroid number are "strong
yellow green" (131) and "Hooker's green No.2" for which they are "moderate
green" (145).

A tabulation of synonymous names is also provided in [Ref.7.3, pp. 37-82].
Under each centroid number are listed the various names assigned in the 14
systems to the same, or approximately the same, color. Under centroid number
183 ("dark blue") there are 91 different names. If we are interested in the

names given to this color in the textile industry, we should consider the
six names listed in the color-sample system of the Textile Color Card Association. Under centroid number 145 ("moderate green") there are 25 names
listed for the Maerz and Paul system. These names include, in addition to
"Hooker's green No.2", the following that are familiar to artists: "Egyptian
green" and "transparent chromium oxide" for two different color samples;
"chrome green", "emeraude", "(French) Veronese green" and "viridian" for one
color sample.

8.9 Color Specification: The Levels of Precision

After considering the discussions of color specification in this book, we
cannot escape realizing that certain systems are more suitable than others
in a given situation. Perhaps the most important aspect that must be recognized is the level of precision that is needed. KELLY has described the following six levels of precision [Ref.7.3, p. A-10]:

First level. The first level pertains to the most general color designations, such as the color "yellow" when one casually indicates the color of
a car. At this level, 10 generic hue names suffice: pink, red, orange, brown,
yellow, olive, yellow green, blue, and purple. In addition, there are (having no hue): white, gray, and black.

Second level. At the second level of precision the list of names is increased by adding 16 intermediate hue names: yellowish pink, reddish orange,
reddish brown, orange yellow, yellowish brown, olive brown, greenish yellow,
olive green, yellowish green, bluish green, greenish blue, purplish blue,
violet, reddish purple, purplish pink, and purplish red. Twenty-six of the
colors (omitting white, gray, and black) are presented as the section titles
in Table 8.3. At this level of precision the color of the car might be said
to be "greenish yellow".

The names for lights proposed by KELLY (Sect.7.1) are at this level of
precision. The foregoing list of color names and the one in Table 7.1 are
similar. Among the color names for lights are, however, orange-pink, blue-
green, and red-purple; necessarily absent are brown, olive, gray, and black.

Third level. At the third level, the aforementioned color categories are
subdivided (Table 8.3) to yield the 267 ISCC-NBS color names. As indicated
in Sect.8.8, Munsell color space is divided into 267 color-name blocks. (At
the second level of precision, Munsell color space is sectioned into 29 large
color-name blocks.)

The color names are generated by addition of terms that suggest the degree of lightness and of saturation. These terms include vivid, brilliant, strong, deep, very deep, very light, light, moderate, dark, very dark, very pale, pale, light grayish, grayish, dark grayish, and blackish. At this level of precision, the color of the car might be found to be "vivid greenish yellow" (centroid number 97). The collection of color cards of the *Standard Color Card of America* (Table 8.1) belongs at this level.

Fourth level. At the fourth level, color space is further subdivided into between 1000 and 10,000 colors. The color-sample systems found at this level of precision include the *Munsell Book of Color*, the *NCS Colour Atlas*, the *DIN-Farbenkarte*, and *The Dictionary of Color* by Maerz and Paul (Table 8.1). It is possible, but rather cumbersome, to employ color names at this level. Numerical or letter codes are preferable, such as the Munsell notation. With the aid of the *Munsell Book of Color*, glossy edition, one might find that the color of the car's paint is, in Munsell notation, 7.5Y 8/12.

Fifth level. The fifth level of precision is demonstrated by visually interpolating between Munsell chips. By this means the number of specified colors can be increased to about 100,000. This is possible, because with great care Value can be estimated to 1/10th of a Munsell Value unit, Chroma to 1/4th of a Chroma unit, and Hue to 1 Hue unit at Chroma 2 or to 1/4 Hue unit at Chroma 10 and higher. Thus, the color of the paint on the car might be found to be 8½Y 8.3/12½.

Sixth level. Finally, at the sixth level of precision, optical instrumentation is required to provide a measurement. Here, the number of color divisions is of the order of 5,000,000. The color of the car paint, now specified by a laboratory, might be CIE 1931 (0.291, 0.433, 0.468), CIE ILL C. These specifications can then be converted to Munsell notation, to comparable accuracy [8.13]: 8.6Y 8.35/.12.6.

Table 8.3. ISCC-NBS color names.
The ISCC-NBS names and centroid numbers for colors of opaque, translucent,
and transparent materials. Exceptionally Nos.9, 92, 153, 189, 231, and 263
present different names (in parentheses) for colors of translucent and transparent materials. This table is based on the one shown on p. 448 in [8.32]

Pink (Pk)

1--vivid Pk
2--strong Pk
3--deep Pk
4--light Pk
5--moderate Pk
6--dark Pk
7--pale Pk
8--grayish Pk
9--pinkish white (faint Pk)
10--pinkish gray

Red (R)

11--vivid R
12--strong R
13--deep R
14--very deep R
15--moderate R
16--dark R
17--very dark R
18--light grayish R
19--grayish R
20--dark grayish R
21--blackish R
22--reddish gray
23--dark reddish gray
24--reddish black

Yellowish pink (yPk)

25--vivid yPk
26--strong yPk
27--deep yPk
28--light yPk
29--moderate yPk
30--dark yPk
31--pale yPk
32--grayish yPk
33--brownish pink

Reddish orange (rO)

34--vivid rO
35--strong rO
36--deep rO
37--moderate rO
38--dark rO
39--grayish rO

Reddish brown (rBr)

40--strong rBr
41--deep rBr
42--light rBr

43--moderate rBr
44--dark rBr
45--light grayish rBr
46--grayish rBr
47--dark grayish rBr

Orange (O)

48--vivid O
49--brilliant O
50--strong O
51--deep O
52--light O
53--moderate O
54--brownish O

Brown (Br)

55--strong Br
56--deep Br
57--light Br
58--moderate Br
59--dark Br
60--light grayish Br
61--grayish Br
62--dark grayish Br
63--light brownish gray
64--brownish gray
65--brownish black

Orange yellow (OY)

66--vivid OY
67--brilliant OY
68--strong OY
69--deep OY
70--light OY
71--moderate OY
72--dark OY
73--pale OY

Yellowish brown (yBr)

74--strong yBr
75--deep yBr
76--light yBr
77--moderate yBr
78--dark yBr
79--light grayish yBr
80--grayish yBr
81--dark grayish yBr

Yellow (Y)

82--vivid Y
83--brilliant Y

84--strong Y
85--deep Y
86--light Y
87--moderate Y
88--dark Y
89--pale Y
90--grayish Y
91--dark grayish Y
92--yellowish white (faint Y)
93--yellowish gray

Olive brown (OlBr)

94--light OlBr
95--moderate OlBr
96--dark OlBr

Greenish yellow (gY)

97--vivid gY
98--brilliant gY
99--strong gY
100--deep gY
101--light gY
102--moderate gY
103--dark gY
104--pale gY
105--grayish gY

Olive (Ol)

106--light Ol
107--moderate Ol
108--dark Ol
109--light grayish Ol
110--grayish Ol
111--dark grayish Ol
112--light Ol gray
113--Ol gray
114--Ol black

Yellow green (YG)

115--vivid YG
116--brilliant YG
117--strong YG
118--deep YG
119--light YG
120--moderate YG
121--pale YG
122--grayish YG

Olive green (OlG)

123--strong OlG
124--deep OlG
125--moderate OlG
126--dark OlG
127--grayish OlG
128--dark grayish OlG

Yellowish green (yG)

129--vivid yG

130--brilliant yG
131--strong yG
132--deep yG
133--very deep yG
134--very light yG
135--light yG
136--moderate yG
137--dark yG
138--very dark yG

Green (G)

139--vivid G
140--brilliant G
141--strong G
142--deep G
143--very light G
144--light G
145--moderate G
146--dark G
147--very dark G
148--very pale G
149--pale G
150--grayish G
151--dark grayish G
152--blackish G
153--greenish white (faint G)
154--light greenish gray
155--greenish gray
156--dark greenish gray
157--greenish black

Bluish green (bG)

158--vivid bG
159--brilliant bG
160--strong bG
161--deep bG
162--very light bG
163--light bG
164--moderate bG
165--dark bG
166--very dark bG

Greenish blue (gB)

167--vivid gB
168--brilliant gB
169--strong gB
170--deep gB
171--very light gB
172--light gB
173--moderate gB
174--dark gB
175--very dark gB

Blue (B)

176--vivid B
177--brilliant B
178--strong B
179--deep B

180--very light B
181--light B
182--moderate B
183--dark B
184--very pale B
185--pale B
186--grayish B
187--dark grayish B
188--blackish B
189--bluish white (faint B)
190--light bluish gray
191--bluish gray
192--dark bluish gray
193--bluish black

Purplish blue (pB)

194--vivid pB
195--brilliant pB
196--strong pB
197--deep pB
198--very light pB
199--light pB
200--moderate pB
201--dark pB
202--very pale pB
203--pale pB
204--grayish pB

Violet (V)

205--vivid V
206--brilliant V
207--strong V
208--deep V
209--very light V
210--light V
211--moderate V
212--dark V
213--very pale V
214--pale V
215--grayish V

Purple (P)

216--vivid P
217--brilliant P
218--strong P
219--deep P
220--very deep P
221--very light P
222--light P
223--moderate P
224--dark P

225--very dark P
226--very pale P
227--pale P
228--grayish P
229--dark grayish P
230--blackish P
231--purplish white (faint P)
232--light purplish gray
233--purplish gray
234--dark purplish gray
235--purplish black

Reddish purple (rP)

236--vivid rP
237--strong rP
238--deep rP
239--very deep rP
240--light rP
241--moderate rP
242--dark rP
243--very dark rP
244--pale rP
245--grayish rP

Purplish pink (pPk)

246--brilliant pPk
247--strong pPk
248--deep pPk
249--light pPk
250--moderate pPk
251--dark pPk
252--pale pPk
253--grayish pPk

Purplish red (pR)

254--vivid pR
255--strong pR
256--deep pR
257--very deep pR
258--moderate pR
259--dark pR
260--very dark pR
261--light grayish pR
262--grayish pR

Neutral colors

263--white (colorless)
264--light gray
265--medium gray
266--dark gray
267--black

Table 8.4. Key for converting a Munsell color notation into an ISCC-NBS centroid number. (See pp.102 and 103 for instructions.)
This table presents in tabular form the information presented in graphical form in 31 *color-name charts* on pages 16-31 of "The ISCC-NBS Method of Designating Colors and a Dictionary of Color Names" by Kenneth L. KELLY and Deane B. JUDD, in *Color — Universal Language and Dictionary of Names* by the same authors. NBS Special Publication 440 (Washington, D.C.: U.S. Government Printing Office, 1976)

```
VALUE                    CHROMA                                  HUE              NO.

         0 0 0 1 1 1 2 2 3 5 6 7 8 9 1 1 1 1 1 4 9 1 4 6 7 8 9 1 2 3 5 7 8
         . . . . . . . .                 0 1 3 4 5 0 R R R R R R Y Y Y Y Y Y
         0 5 7 0 2 5 0 5                             P     R R R R R R
─────────────────────────────────────────────────────────────────────────────────
8.5-10. 0 0 . . . . . . . . . . . . . . . . . . . . 0 0 0 0 0 0 0 0 0 0 0 0 . 263
8.5-10. 0 0 . . . . . . . . . . . . . . . . . . . . . . . . . . . . . . . 0 0 263
8.5-10. . 0 0 0 0 0 . . . . . . . . . . . . . . . 0 0 0 0 0 0 0 0 0 0 0 . .   9
8.5-10. . 0 0 0 0 . . . . . . . . . . . . . . . . . . . . . . . . . . 0 0 . .   9
8.0-10. . . . . . 0 0 0 0 . . . . . . . . . . . . 0 0 0 0 . . . . . . . . .   7
8.0-10. . . . . . . . 0 0 0 0 . . . . . . . . . . 0 0 0 0 . . . . . . . . .   4
8.0-10. . . . . . 0 0 0 0 . . . . . . . . . . . . . 0 0 0 0 0 0 0 0 . . .  31
8.0-10. . . . . . 0 0 0 0 0 . . . . . . . . . . . . . . . . . . . . . 0 0 0  31
8.0-10. . . . . . . . 0 0 0 0 . . . . . . . . . . . 0 0 0 0 0 0 . . . .  28
8.0-10. . . . . . . . 0 0 0 . . . .. . . . . . . . . . . . . 0 0 0 0 .  28
7.5-10. . . . . . . 0 0 0 0 0 . . . . . . . . . . . . . . . . 0 0 0 0 .  52
7.5-10. . . . . . . . . 0 0 0 0 . . . . . . . . . . . . . . . 0 0 0 0 .  49
6.5-10. . . . . . . 0 0 0 0 0 . . . . . . . 0 0 0 0 0 0 . . . . .  26
6.5-10. . . . . . . . . 0 0 0 0 0 . . 0 0 0 0 0 0 0 . . . .  25
6.5-8.5 0 0 . . . . . . . . . . . . . . . . 0 0 0 0 0 0 0 0 0 0 0 0 . 264
6.5-8.5 0 0 0 . . . . . . . . . . . . . . . . . . . . . . . . . . . 0 0 264
6.5-8.5 . 0 0 0 0 0 . . . . . . . . . . . . . 0 0 0 0 0 0 0 0 0 0 0 . .  10
6.5-8.5 . 0 0 0 0 . . . . . . . . . . . . . . . . . . . . . . . 0 0 .  10
6.5-8.0 . . . . . 0 0 0 0 . . . . . . . . . . 0 0 0 . . . . . . .   8
6.5-8.0 . . . . . . 0 0 0 0 . . . . . . . . . 0 0 0 . . . . . . .   5
6.5-10. . . . . . . . . 0 0 0 0 0 . . . . 0 0 0 . . . . . .   2
6.5-10. . . . . . . . . 0 0 0 0 0 0 0 0 . . . . . . . .   1
6.5-8.0 . . . . . 0 0 0 0 . . . . . . . . . . 0 0 0 0 0 0 0 0 . .  32
6.5-8.0 . . . . . . 0 0 0 0 . . . . . . . . . . 0 0 0 0 0 0 . . .  29
6.5-8.0 . . . . . . 0 0 0 . . . . . . . . . . . . 0 0 0 0 .  29
6.5-8.0 . . . . 0 0 0 0 0 . . . . . . . . . . . . . 0 0 0  33
6.5-7.5 . . . . . . 0 0 0 0 . . . . . . . . . . . . 0 0 .  53
5.5-6.5 . . . . . . . 0 0 0 0 . . . . . . . . . . . 0 0 .  53
5.5-7.5 . . . . . . 0 0 0 0 . . . . . . . . . . . 0 0 0 .  53
5.5-7.5 . . . . . . . . 0 0 0 0 . . . . . . . . . 0 0 0 0 .  50
5.5-6.5 . . . . 0 0 0 0 0 . . . . . . . . . 0 0 0 0 . . . . .  18
5.5-6.5 . . . . . 0 0 0 0 . . . . . . . . . . 0 0 0 . . . . .  18
5.5-6.5 . . . . . . 0 0 0 . . . . . . . . 0 0 0 0 . . . . .   6
5.5-6.5 . . . . . . . 0 0 0 0 0 0 0 0 . 0 0 0 . . . . . .   3
5.5-6.5 . . . . . . . 0 0 0 0 0 . . . . . . 0 0 . . . . . .   3
5.5-6.5 . . . . . . . . 0 0 0 0 . . . . . 0 0 . . . . . .  27
5.5-6.5 . . . . . . 0 0 0 0 0 0 0 0 . . . 0 0 . . . . . .  27
5.5-6.5 . . . . . . 0 0 0 . . . . . . . . 0 0 0 . . . .  30
5.5-6.5 . . . . . . . . . . . . . 0 0 . 0 0 0 0 . . . . . .  11
4.5-6.5 0 0 . . . . . . . . . . . . . . . . 0 0 0 0 0 0 0 0 0 0 0 0 . 265
4.5-6.5 0 0 0 . . . . . . . . . . . . . . . . . . . . . . . . . . . 0 0 265
4.5-6.5 . 0 0 0 0 0 . . . . . . . . . . . . . . 0 0 0 0 0 0 0 . . . .  22
4.5-6.5 . . . . . . 0 0 0 0 0 . . . . . . . 0 0 0 0 0 . . . .  37
4.5-6.5 . . . . . . . . 0 0 . . . . . . . . 0 0 0 0 0 . . . .  35
4.5-6.5 . . . . . . . 0 0 0 0 . . . . . . . 0 0 0 . . . .  34
4.5-6.5 . . . . . . 0 0 . . . . . . . . . . 0 0 0 0 . . .  42
4.5-6.5 . . . . . . . 0 0 0 . . . . . . . . 0 0 0 0 . . .  39
4.5-6.5 . . . . . . 0 0 0 0 . . . . . . . . . . 0 0 0 . .  45
4.5-6.5 . 0 0 0 0 0 . . . . . . . . . . . . . . . . 0 0 0 . .  63
4.5-6.5 . 0 0 0 0 . . . . . . . . . . . . . . . . . 0 0 .  63
4.5-6.5 . . 0 0 0 . . . . . . . . . . . . . . . . . 0 0  63
4.5-6.5 . . . . . . 0 0 0 . . . . . . . . . . . . 0 0 0 0  57
4.5-6.5 . . . . 0 0 0 0 0 . . . . . . . . . . . . . 0 0 0  60
─────────────────────────────────────────────────────────────────────────────────
```

Table 8.4 (continued)

```
VALUE              CHROMA                                HUE              NO.
        0 0 0 1 1 2 2 3 5 6 7 8 9 1 1 1 1 1 4 9 1 4 6 7 8 9 1 2 3 5 7 8
        . . . . . . .             0 1 3 4 5 0 R R R R R R Y Y Y Y Y Y
        0 5 7 0 2 5 0 5                       P   R R R R R

3.5-6.5 . . . . . O . . . . . . . . . O O O O . . . . . . O O O . . . . .  34
4.5-5.5 . . . . . O O O O . . . . . . . . . . . . . . . . O O O . . . . .  19
4.5-5.5 . . . . . . . . . O O O O . . . . . . . . . . . . . O O . . . . .  54
4.5-5.5 . . . . . . . . O O O O O . . . . . . . . . . . . . O O O . . . .  54
4.5-5.5 . . . . . . . . . . O O O O . . . . . . . . . . . . O O O O . . .  51
4.5-10. . . . . . . . . . . O O O . . . . . . . . . . . . . O O O O . . .  48
3.5-5.5 . . . . O O O O O O O . . . . . . . . O O O O O . . . . . . . . .  19
3.5-5.5 . . . . . . . . O O O O O . . . . . . . O O O O . . . . . . . . .  15
3.5-5.5 . . . . . . . . . O O . . . . . . . . . O O O O . . . . . . . . .  12
3.5-5.5 . . . . . . . . O O O O . . . . . . . . O O O O . . . . . . . . .  11
3.5-4.5 . . . . . . . . O O O O . . . . . . . . . O O O . . . . . . . . .  11
3.5-4.5 . . . . . . . . O O O O . . . . . . . . . O O O O . . . . . . . .  38
3.5-4.5 . . . . . . . . . O O . . . . . . . . . O O O O O . . . . . . . .  36
2.5-4.5 O O . . . . . . . . . . . . . . . . . O O O O O O O O O O O O O O 266
2.5-4.5 . O O O O O . . . . . . . . . . . . . O O O O O O . . . . . . . .  23
2.5-4.5 . O O O O O . . . . . . . . . . . . . . . . . . . O O O O . . . .  64
2.5-4.5 . O O O O . . . . . . . . . . . . . . . . . . . . . O O O . . . .  64
2.5-4.5 . . . . . . . O O O O O O O O O O O O . . . . . . O O O O . . . .  55
2.5-4.5 . . . . . O O O . . . . . . . . . . . . . . . . . O O . . . . . .  61
2.5-4.5 . . . . O O O O . . . . . . . . . . . . . . . . . . O O O . . . .  61
2.5-4.5 . . . . . . O O O . . . . . . . . . . . . . . . . . . O O O O . .  58
2.5-4.5 . . . . O O O O . . . . . . . . . . . . . . . O O O O O . . . . .  46
2.5-4.5 . . . . . . O O O O . . . . . . . . . . . . . . O O O O . . . . .  43
2.5-4.5 . . . . . . O O . . . . . . . . . . . . . . . . . O O O . . . . .  43
2.5-3.5 . . . . O O O O . . . . . . . . . . . . . . O O O . . . . . . . .  46
2.5-3.5 . . . . . . O O O O . . . . . . . . . . . . O O O . . . . . . . .  43
2.5-3.5 . . . . . . . . O O O O O O O O O O O . . . . . . O O O . . . . .  40
2.5-3.5 . . . . O O O O . . . . . . . . . . . O O O . . . . . . . . . . .  20
2.0-2.5 . O O O O O O O O . . . . . . . . . . O O O . . . . . . . . . . .  20
2.0-3.5 . . . . . . . O O O O O O . . . . . . O O O . . . . . . . . . . .  16
2.0-3.5 . . . . . . . . . O O O . . . . . . . . O O O O . . . . . . . . .  16
2.0-3.5 . . . . . . . . . . O O O . . . . . O O O O O . . . . . . . . . .  13
1.5-2.5 . O O O O O O O O . . . . . . . . . . O O O O O O O . . . . . . .  47
1.5-2.5 . . . . . . . O O . . . . . . . . . . O O O O O O O . . . . . . .  44
1.5-2.5 . O O O O O O O . . . . . . . . . . . . . . . . . . . . O O O O .  62
1.5-2.5 . . . . . . O O O . . . . . . . . . . . . . . . . . . . O O O O .  59
0.0-3.5 . . . . . . . . . . O O O O O . O O O O O O . . . . . . . . . . .  11
0.0-2.5 O O . . . . . . . . . . . . . . . . . O O O O O O O O O O O O O O 267
0.0-2.5 . . . . . . . . O O O . . . . . . . . O O O O . . . . . . . . . .  41
0.0-2.5 . . . . . . O O O O O O O O O O O O . . . . . . O O O . . . . . .  41
0.0-2.5 . . . . . . O O O O O O O O O O O O . . . . . . . O O O O . . . .  56
0.0-2.0 . O O O . . . . . . . . . . . . . . O O O . . . . . . . . . . . .  24
0.0-2.0 . . . O O O O . . . . . . . . . . . O O O . . . . . . . . . . . .  21
0.0-2.0 . . . . . . O O O O O O . . . . . . O O O . . . . . . . . . . . .  17
0.0-2.0 . . . . . . . . O O O O O . . . . . O O O O O . . . . . . . . . .  14
0.0-1.5 . O O O . . . . . . . . . . . . . . O O O O O . . . O . . . . . .  24
0.0-1.5 . . . O O O O O O . . . . . . . . . O O O O O O O . . . . . . . .  44
0.0-1.5 . O O O . . . . . . . . . . . . . . . . . . . . . O O O O O . . .  65
0.0-1.5 . . . O O O O O O . . . . . . . . . . . . . . . . . . . O O O O .  59
```

Table 8.4 (continued)

```
VALUE                    CHROMA                              HUE          NO.
        0 0 0 1 1 1 2 2 3 5 6 7 8 9 1 1 1 1 1 4   7 8 1 4 7 9 2 4 8
        . . . . . . . .               0 1 3 4 5 0 Y Y Y Y Y Y Y G G G
        0 5 7 0 2 5 0 5                           R R           Y Y Y
─────────────────────────────────────────────────────────────────────────
8.5-10.  0 0 0 . . . . . . . . . . . . . . . . .   0 0 0 0 0 0 . . .   263
8.5-10.  0 0 . . . . . . . . . . . . . . . . . .   . . . . . 0 0 0 0   263
8.5-10.  . . 0 0 0 . . . . . . . . . . . . . . .   0 0 . . . . . . .    92
8.5-10.  . . 0 0 0 0 0 . . . . . . . . . . . . .   . 0 0 0 0 0 . . .    92
8.5-10.  . 0 0 0 0 . . . . . . . . . . . . . . .   . . . . . 0 0 0 .    92
8.0-10.  . . . . . . . . 0 0 0 0 0 . . . . . . .   0 0 0 . . . . . .    70
8.0-10.  . . . . . . . . . . . 0 0 0 0 . . . . .   0 0 0 . . . . . .    67
8.0-10.  . . . . . 0 0 0 0 . . . . . . . . . . .   . . 0 0 0 . . . .    89
8.0-10.  . . . . . 0 0 0 . . . . . . . . . . . .   . . . . 0 0 . . .    89
8.0-10.  . . . . . . . 0 0 0 0 . . . . . . . . .   . . 0 0 0 . . . .    86
8.0-10.  . . . . . . . . . 0 0 0 0 . . . . . . .   . . 0 0 0 . . . .    83
8.0-10.  . . . . . . 0 0 . . . . . . . . . . . .   . . . 0 0 0 . . .   104
8.0-10.  . . . . . . . 0 0 0 0 . . . . . . . . .   . . . 0 0 0 . . .   101
8.0-10.  . . . . . . . . . 0 0 0 0 . . . . . . .   . . . 0 0 0 . . .    98
7.5-10.  . . . . . . 0 0 0 . . . . . . . . . . .   0 0 . . . . . . .    73
7.5-10.  . . . . 0 0 0 0 0 . . . . . . . . . . .   . 0 0 . . . . . .    73
7.5-10.  . . . 0 0 0 0 0 . . . . . . . . . . . .   . . . . 0 0 0 0     121
7.5-10.  . . . . . 0 0 0 0 . . . . . . . . . . .   . . . . . 0 0 0     119
7.5-10.  . . . . . . . 0 0 0 0 0 . . . . . . . .   . . . . . 0 0 0     116
5.5-10.  . . . . . . . . . . . . 0 0 0 . . . . .   0 0 0 . . . . . .    66
5.5-10.  . . . . . . . . . . 0 0 0 0 0 . . . . .   . . 0 0 0 . . . .    82
5.5-10.  . . . . . . . . . . 0 0 0 0 0 . . . . .   . . . . 0 0 0 . .    97
3.5-10.  . . . . . . . . . . 0 0 0 0 0 . . . . .   . . . . . 0 0 0     115
6.5-8.5  0 0 0 . . . . . . . . . . . . . . . . .   0 0 0 0 0 0 . . .   264
6.5-8.5  0 0 . . . . . . . . . . . . . . . . . .   . . . . . 0 0 0 0   264
6.5-8.5  . . 0 0 0 . . . . . . . . . . . . . . .   0 0 . . . . . . .    93
6.5-8.5  . . 0 0 0 0 0 . . . . . . . . . . . . .   . 0 0 0 0 0 . . .    93
6.5-8.5  . 0 0 0 0 . . . . . . . . . . . . . . .   . . . . . 0 0 0 .    93
6.5-8.0  . . . . . . . . 0 0 0 0 0 . . . . . . .   0 0 0 . . . . . .    71
6.5-8.0  . . . . . . . . . . . 0 0 0 0 . . . . .   0 0 0 . . . . . .    68
6.5-8.0  . . . . . 0 0 0 0 . . . . . . . . . . .   . . 0 0 0 . . . .    90
6.5-8.0  . . . . . 0 0 0 . . . . . . . . . . . .   . . . . 0 0 . . .    90
6.5-8.0  . . . . . . . 0 0 0 0 . . . . . . . . .   . . 0 0 0 . . . .    87
6.5-8.0  . . . . . . . . . 0 0 0 0 . . . . . . .   . . 0 0 0 . . . .    84
6.5-8.0  . . . . . . 0 0 . . . . . . . . . . . .   . . . 0 0 0 . . .   105
6.5-8.0  . . . . . . . 0 0 0 0 . . . . . . . . .   . . . 0 0 0 . . .   102
6.5-8.0  . . . . . . . . . 0 0 0 0 . . . . . . .   . . . 0 0 0 . . .    99
6.5-7.5  . . . . . . 0 0 0 . . . . . . . . . . .   0 0 . . . . . . .    76
6.5-7.5  . . . . 0 0 0 0 0 . . . . . . . . . . .   . 0 0 . . . . . .    79
6.5-7.5  . . . 0 0 0 0 0 . . . . . . . . . . . .   . . . . 0 0 . . .   122
5.5-7.5  . . . . 0 0 0 . . . . . . . . . . . . .   . 0 0 . . . . . .    76
5.5-6.5  . . . . . . . . 0 0 0 0 0 . . . . . . .   0 0 0 . . . . . .    72
5.5-6.5  . . . . . . . . . . . 0 0 0 0 . . . . .   0 0 0 . . . . . .    69
5.5-6.5  . . . 0 0 0 0 0 . . . . . . . . . . . .   . 0 0 . . . . . .    79
5.5-6.5  . . . 0 0 0 0 0 . . . . . . . . . . . .   . . 0 0 . . . . .    94
5.5-6.5  . . . . . . 0 0 . . . . . . . . . . . .   . . 0 0 0 . . . .    91
5.5-6.5  . . . . . . . . 0 0 0 0 . . . . . . . .   . . 0 0 0 . . . .    88
5.5-6.5  . . . . . . . . . 0 0 0 0 . . . . . . .   . . 0 0 0 . . . .    85
5.5-6.5  . . . . . . 0 0 . . . . . . . . . . . .   . . . . 0 0 0 . .   106
5.5-6.5  . . . . . . . 0 0 0 0 . . . . . . . . .   . . . . 0 0 0 . .   103
5.5-6.5  . . . . . . . . . 0 0 0 0 . . . . . . .   . . . . 0 0 0 . .   100
```

Table 8.4 (continued)

VALUE	0.0	0.5	0.7	1.0	1.2	1.5	2.0	2.5	3	5	6	7	8	9	10	11	13	14	15	40	7YR	8YR	1Y	4Y	7Y	9Y	2GY	4GY	8GY	NO.
4.5-7.5					0	0	0	0	0																		0	0	0	122
4.5-7.5								0	0	0	0																0	0	0	120
4.5-7.5											0	0	0	0	0												0	0	0	117
4.5-6.5	0	0	0																		0	0	0	0	0	0				265
4.5-6.5	0	0																								0	0	0	0	265
4.5-6.5			0	0	0																0	0	0	0						63
4.5-6.5			0	0	0	0	0																	0	0	0				112
4.5-6.5		0	0	0	0																						0	0	0	112
4.5-6.5						0	0	0																0	0	0				109
4.5-6.5					0	0	0	0	0																	0	0			109
4.5-5.5								0	0	0	0	0	0	0	0	0					0	0								74
4.5-5.5					0	0	0	0	0													0	0							80
4.5-5.5						0	0															0	0							77
4.5-5.5					0	0	0	0	0	0	0	0	0	0	0	0	0	0					0	0						94
4.5-5.5								0	0	0	0	0	0	0	0	0	0	0						0	0	0	0			106
3.5-5.5							0	0	0	0	0	0	0	0	0	0	0	0				0	0							74
3.5-4.5					0	0	0	0														0	0							80
3.5-4.5						0	0	0														0	0							77
3.5-4.5								0	0	0	0	0															0	0	0	118
2.5-4.5	0	0																			0	0	0	0	0	0	0	0	0	266
2.5-4.5		0	0	0	0																0	0	0	0						64
2.5-4.5					0	0	0	0	0	0	0	0	0	0	0	0	0	0	0	0			0	0						95
2.5-4.5		0	0	0	0	0																		0	0	0				113
2.5-4.5		0	0	0	0																					0	0	0		113
2.5-4.5						0	0	0	0															0	0	0	0			110
2.5-4.5					0	0	0	0	0	0																0	0			110
2.5-4.5								0	0	0	0	0	0	0	0	0	0	0	0					0	0	0	0			107
2.5-4.5						0	0	0	0	0																	0	0	0	127
2.5-4.5							0	0	0	0																	0	0	0	125
2.5-3.5										0	0	0	0	0	0	0	0	0					0	0						123
2.5-3.5					0	0	0	0														0	0							81
1.5-3.5								0	0	0												0	0							78
1.5-2.5		0	0	0	0	0	0	0														0	0							81
1.5-2.5		0	0	0	0	0	0	0	0	0	0	0	0	0	0	0	0	0					0	0						96
1.5-2.5		0	0	0	0	0	0	0	0															0	0	0	0			111
1.5-2.5									0	0	0	0	0	0	0	0	0	0						0	0	0	0			108
1.5-2.5		0	0	0	0	0	0	0	0																		0	0	0	128
1.5-2.5								0	0	0	0																0	0	0	126
0.0-3.5										0	0	0	0	0	0	0	0	0	0			0	0							75
0.0-2.5											0	0	0	0	0	0	0	0	0							0	0	0		124
0.0-1.5				0	0	0	0	0	0													0	0							78
0.0-1.5		0	0	0																	0	0	0	0						65
0.0-1.5				0	0	0	0	0	0	0	0	0	0	0	0	0	0	0	0	0			0	0						96
0.0-1.5				0	0	0	0	0	0	0	0	0	0	0	0	0	0	0	0	0				0	0	0				108
0.0-1.5		0	0	0																				0	0	0	0	0		114
0.0-1.5				0	0	0	0	0	0	0																	0	0	0	126
0.0-2.5	0	0																			0	0	0	0	0	0	0	0	0	267

Table 8.4 (continued)

VALUE	0.0	0.5	0.7	1.0	1.2	1.5	2.0	2.5	3	5	6	7	8	9	10	11	13	14	15	40	4GY	8GY	3G	9G	10BG	9B	5PB	6PB	7PB	9PB	NO.
8.5–10.	0	0																			0	0	0	0	0	0	0	0	0	0	263
8.5–10.		0	0	0	0																0	0	0	0	0						153
8.5–10.							0	0	0	0	0											0	0								134
8.5–10.		0	0	0	0	0																			0	0	0	0	0	0	189
7.5–10.					0	0	0	0															0	0	0						148
7.5–10.							0	0	0	0	0												0	0							143
7.5–10.							0	0	0	0	0													0	0						162
7.5–10.						0	0	0	0																0	0					184
7.5–10.							0	0	0	0	0															0	0				184
7.5–10.						0	0	0	0																		0	0	0	0	184
7.5–10.								0	0	0	0															0	0				171
7.5–10.									0	0	0	0															0	0			180
7.5–10.										0	0	0															0	0	0		180
7.5–10.								Q	0																		0	0	0	0	202
7.5–10.									0	0	0																	0	0	0	198
7.5–10.								0	0	0	0	0																	0	0	198
6.5–10.									0	0	0	0	0									0	0								130
5.5–10.									0	0	0	0	0										0	0							140
5.5–10.										0	0	0	0	0										0	0						159
5.5–10.										0	0	0	0	0										0	0						168
5.5–10.											0	0	0	0												0	0	0	0		177
5.5–10.											0	0	0	0															0	0	195
4.5–10.												0	0	0	0	0							0	0							129
3.0–10.												0	0	0	0											0	0	0	0		176
3.0–10.												0	0	0	0														0	0	194
0.0–10.												0	0	0	0	0								0	0						139
0.0–10.												0	0	0	0	0									0	0					158
0.0–10.												0	0	0	0	0									0	0					167
6.5–8.5		0	0	0	0																0	0	0	0							154
6.5–8.5						0	0	0	0	0												0	0								135
6.5–8.5		0	0	0	0	0																				0	0	0	0	0	190
6.5–8.5	0	0																			0	0	0	0	0	0	0	0	0	0	264
5.5–7.5				0	0	0	0																0	0							149
5.5–7.5						Q	0	0	0	0													0	0							144
5.5–7.5						0	0	0	0	0														0	0						163
5.5–7.5						0	0	0	0																0	0					185
5.5–7.5						0	0	0	0	0																	0	0	0	0	185
5.5–7.5						0	0	0	0																	0	0				185
5.5–7.5								0	0	0	0															0	0				172
5.5–7.5									0	0	0	0															0	0			181
5.5–7.5										0	0	0															0	0	0		181
4.5–7.5									0	0																	0	0	0	0	203
4.5–7.5									0	0	0																0	0	0		199
4.5–7.5									0	0	0	0																	0	0	199
4.5–6.5								0	0	0	0													0	0						136
4.5–6.5										0	0	0	0											0	0						131
4.5–6.5		0	0	0	0																0	0	0	0							155
4.5–6.5		0	0	0	0	0																				0	0	0	0	0	191
4.5–6.5	0	0																			0	0	0	0	0	0	0	0	0	0	265
4.5–5.5											0	0	0														0	0	0		182
4.5–5.5											0	0	0																0	0	195
4.5–5.5													0	0															0	0	196
4.5–5.5								0	0	0	0	0														0	0				145
3.5–5.5										0	0	0	0	0												0	0				141
3.5–5.5				0	0	0	0																0	0	0	0					150

Table 8.4 (continued)

VALUE	0.0	0.5	0.7	1.0	1.2	1.5	2.0	2.5	3	5	6	7	8	9	10	11	13	14	15	40	4GY	8GY	3G	9G	10BG	9B	5PB	6PB	7PB	9PB	NO.
3.5–5.5								O	O	O	O	O												O	O						164
3.5–5.5										O	O	O	O	O										O	O						160
3.5–5.5								O	O	O	O														O	O					173
3.5–5.5									O	O	O	O	O												O	O					169
3.0–5.5						O	O	O	O																O	O					186
3.0–5.5						O	O	O	O	O																O	O				186
3.0–5.5						O	O	O	O																		O	O	O	O	186
3.0–5.5								O	O	O	O	O													O	O					182
3.0–5.5										O	O	O	O													O	O	O			178
3.0–4.5								O	O	O	O	O														O	O	O			182
3.0–4.5							O	O																		O	O				204
3.0–4.5										O	O	O	O																O	O	196
3.0–4.5								O	O	O	O	O																	O	O	200
2.5–4.5								O	O	O	O	O										O	O								137
2.5–4.5										O	O	O	O	O	O	O	O	O	O	O		O	O								132
2.5–4.5							O	O																				O	O	O	204
2.5–4.5		O	O	O	O																O	O	O	O	O						156
2.5–4.5		O	O	O	O	O																			O	O	O	O	O	O	192
2.5–4.5	O	O																			O	O	O	O	O	O	O	O	O	O	266
2.5–3.5					O	O	O	O														O	O	O	O						151
2.5–3.5							O	O	O	O	O												O	O							146
2.5–3.5							O	O	O	O	O												O	O							165
2.5–3.5							O	O	O	O													O	O							174
2.5–3.0						O	O	O	O															O	O	O	O	O	O		187
2.5–3.0							O	O	O	O																O	O	O			183
2.0–3.0								O	O	O																			O	O	200
2.0–2.5		O	O	O	O	O	O																O	O	O	O					151
2.0–2.5							O	O	O	O	O	O											O	O							146
2.0–2.5							O	O	O	O	O	O											O	O							165
2.0–2.5		O	O	O	O	O	O																	O	O	O	O	O	O		187
2.0–2.5							O	O	O	O	O	O											O	O							174
2.0–2.5							O	O	O	O																		O	O	O	204
0.0–3.5										O	O	O	O	O									O	O							142
0.0–3.5										O	O	O	O	O									O	O							161
0.0–3.5										O	O	O	O	O									O	O							170
0.0–3.0								O	O	O																	O	O	O		183
0.0–3.0										O	O	O	O	O												O	O	O	O		179
0.0–3.0													O	O	O	O	O									O	O	O	O		176
0.0–3.0														O	O	O	O	O											O	O	194
0.0–3.0										O	O	O	O	O															O	O	197
0.0–2.5							O	O	O	O	O	O										O	O								138
0.0–2.5										O	O	O	O	O	O	O	O	O	O	O		O	O								133
0.0–2.5							O	O	O	O	O	O														O	O	O			183
0.0–2.5	O	O																			O	O	O	O	O	O	O	O	O	O	267
0.0–2.0							O	O	O	O	O	O											O	O							147
0.0–2.0							O	O	O	O	O	O											O	O							166
0.0–2.0							O	O	O	O	O	O											O	O							175
0.0–2.0							O	O	O	O																		O	O		201
0.0–2.0							O	O	O	O	O	O																	O	O	201
0.0–2.0		O	O	O																				O	O	O	O	O	O		193
0.0–2.0				O	O	O	O																	O	O	O	O	O	O		188
0.0–2.0				O	O	O	O																	O	O	O	O				152
0.0–2.0		O	O	O																				O	O	O	O				157
0.0–1.5		O	O	O																	O	O									157

Table 8.4 (continued)

VALUE	CHROMA																				HUE						NO.
	0.0	0.5	0.7	1.0	1.2	1.5	2.0	2.5	3	5	6	7	8	9	10	11	13	14	15	40	9PB	3P	9P	3RP	9RP	1R	
8.5-10.	0	0	.	.	.	.	.	.	.	.	.	.	.	.	.	.	.	.	.	.	0	0	0	0	0	0	263
8.5-10.	.	0	0	0	0	0	.	.	.	.	.	.	.	.	.	.	.	.	.	.	0	0	0	0	0	.	231
7.5-10.	.	.	.	0	0	0	0	.	.	.	.	.	.	.	.	.	.	.	.	.	0	0	.	.	.	.	226
7.5-10.	.	.	.	.	0	0	0	0	.	.	.	.	.	.	.	.	.	.	.	.	.	0	0	.	.	.	226
7.5-10.	.	.	.	.	.	.	0	0	.	.	.	.	.	.	.	.	.	.	.	.	0	0	.	.	.	.	213
7.5-10.	.	.	.	.	.	.	.	.	0	0	0	0	0	.	.	.	.	.	.	.	0	0	.	.	.	.	209
7.5-10.	.	.	.	.	.	.	.	.	0	0	0	0	0	.	.	.	.	.	.	.	.	0	0	.	.	.	221
7.5-10.	.	.	.	.	.	0	0	0	0	0	.	.	.	.	.	.	.	.	.	.	.	.	0	0	0	.	252
7.5-10.	.	.	.	.	.	.	.	.	0	0	0	0	0	.	.	.	.	.	.	.	.	.	0	0	0	.	249
7.5-10.	.	.	.	.	.	.	.	.	.	.	.	0	0	0	0	0	0	0	.	.	.	.	0	0	0	.	246
5.5-10.	.	.	.	.	.	.	.	.	0	0	0	0	.	.	.	.	.	.	.	.	.	0	0	.	.	.	217
4.5-10.	.	.	.	.	.	.	.	.	0	0	0	0	.	.	.	.	.	.	.	.	0	0	.	.	.	.	206
0.0-10.	.	.	.	.	.	.	.	.	.	.	.	.	.	.	0	0	0	0	.	.	0	0	.	.	.	.	205
0.0-10.	.	.	.	.	.	.	.	.	.	.	.	.	.	.	0	0	0	0	.	.	.	0	0	.	.	.	216
6.5-8.5	.	0	0	0	0	0	.	.	.	.	.	.	.	.	.	.	.	.	.	.	0	0	0	0	0	.	232
6.5-8.5	0	0	.	.	.	.	.	.	.	.	.	.	.	.	.	.	.	.	.	.	0	0	0	0	0	0	264
6.5-7.5	.	.	.	0	0	0	0	.	.	.	.	.	.	.	.	.	.	.	.	.	.	.	0	0	0	.	253
6.5-7.5	.	.	.	.	.	.	0	0	0	0	0	.	.	.	.	.	.	.	.	.	.	.	0	0	0	.	250
6.5-7.5	.	.	.	.	.	.	.	.	0	0	0	0	0	0	.	.	.	.	.	.	.	.	0	0	0	.	247
5.5-7.5	.	.	.	.	0	0	0	0	.	.	.	.	.	.	.	.	.	.	.	.	0	0	.	.	.	.	227
5.5-7.5	.	.	.	.	0	0	0	0	0	.	.	.	.	.	.	.	.	.	.	.	.	0	0	.	.	.	227
5.5-7.5	.	.	.	.	.	.	.	0	0	0	0	0	.	.	.	.	.	.	.	.	.	0	0	.	.	.	222
4.5-7.5	.	.	.	.	.	0	0	.	.	.	.	.	.	.	.	.	.	.	.	.	0	0	.	.	.	.	214
4.5-7.5	.	.	.	.	.	.	0	0	0	0	0	.	.	.	.	.	.	.	.	.	0	0	.	.	.	.	210
4.5-6.5	.	0	0	0	0	0	.	.	.	.	.	.	.	.	.	.	.	.	.	.	0	0	0	0	0	0	233
4.5-6.5	0	0	.	.	.	.	.	.	.	.	.	.	.	.	.	.	.	.	.	.	0	0	0	0	0	0	265
5.5-6.5	.	.	.	.	0	0	0	0	.	.	.	.	.	.	.	.	.	.	.	.	.	.	0	0	0	0	227
5.5-6.5	.	.	.	.	.	.	.	0	0	.	.	.	.	.	.	.	.	.	.	.	.	.	0	0	.	.	244
5.5-6.5	.	.	.	.	.	.	.	.	0	0	0	0	0	.	.	.	.	.	.	.	.	.	0	0	.	.	240
5.5-6.5	.	.	.	.	.	.	.	.	.	.	0	0	0	0	0	0	.	.	.	.	.	.	0	0	.	.	248
5.5-6.5	.	.	.	.	.	.	.	.	.	.	.	.	.	.	.	.	0	0	.	.	.	.	0	0	.	.	236
5.5-6.5	.	.	.	.	.	.	.	0	0	.	.	.	.	.	.	.	.	.	.	.	.	.	.	0	0	0	261
5.5-6.5	.	.	.	.	.	.	.	.	0	0	0	0	0	.	.	.	.	.	.	.	.	.	0	0	.	.	251
5.5-6.5	.	.	.	.	.	.	.	.	.	.	.	.	.	.	.	.	0	0	.	.	.	.	.	0	0	0	254
3.5-5.5	.	.	.	.	0	0	0	0	.	.	.	.	.	.	.	.	.	.	.	.	0	0	.	.	.	.	228
3.5-5.5	.	.	.	.	0	0	0	0	0	.	.	.	.	.	.	.	.	.	.	.	.	0	0	.	.	.	228
3.5-5.5	.	.	.	.	0	0	0	0	.	.	.	.	.	.	.	.	.	.	.	.	.	.	0	0	0	0	228
3.5-5.5	.	.	.	.	.	.	.	.	0	0	0	0	0	.	.	.	.	.	.	.	.	0	0	.	.	.	223
3.5-5.5	.	.	.	.	.	.	.	.	.	.	0	0	0	0	.	.	.	.	.	.	.	0	0	.	.	.	218
3.5-5.5	.	.	.	.	.	.	.	0	0	.	.	.	.	.	.	.	.	.	.	.	.	.	0	0	.	.	245
3.5-5.5	.	.	.	.	.	.	.	.	0	0	0	0	0	.	.	.	.	.	.	.	.	.	0	0	.	.	241
3.5-5.5	.	.	.	.	.	.	.	.	.	.	0	0	0	0	.	.	.	.	.	.	.	.	0	0	.	.	237
3.5-5.5	.	.	.	.	.	.	.	0	0	0	0	.	.	.	.	.	.	.	.	.	.	.	.	0	0	0	262
3.5-5.5	.	.	.	.	.	.	.	.	.	0	0	0	0	0	.	.	.	.	.	.	.	.	.	0	0	0	258
3.5-5.5	.	.	.	.	.	.	.	.	.	.	.	.	0	0	.	.	.	.	.	.	.	.	.	0	0	0	255
2.5-4.5	.	.	.	.	.	.	.	0	0	.	.	.	.	.	.	.	.	.	.	.	0	0	.	.	.	.	215
2.5-4.5	.	.	.	.	.	.	.	.	0	0	0	0	0	.	.	.	.	.	.	.	0	0	.	.	.	.	211
2.5-4.5	.	.	.	.	.	.	.	.	.	.	0	0	0	0	.	.	.	.	.	.	0	0	.	.	.	.	207
2.5-4.5	.	0	0	0	0	0	.	.	.	.	.	.	.	.	.	.	.	.	.	.	0	0	0	0	0	0	234
2.5-4.5	0	0	.	.	.	.	.	.	.	.	.	.	.	.	.	.	.	.	.	.	0	0	0	0	0	0	266

Table 8.4 (continued)

VALUE	0.0	0.5	0.7	1.0	1.2	1.5	2.0	2.5	3	5	6	7	8	9	10	11	13	14	15	40	9PB	3P	9P	3RP	9RP	1R	NO.
2.5–3.5						O	O	O	O												O	O	O	O	O	O	229
2.5–3.5								O	O	O	O											O	O				224
2.5–3.5								O	O	O	O												O	O			242
2.5–3.5								O	O	O	O	O	O	O										O	O	O	259
2.0–5.5													O	O	O	O								O	O	O	254
2.0–3.5											O	O	O	O	O	O						O	O				219
2.0–3.5											O	O	O	O	O	O							O	O			238
2.0–3.5													O	O	O	O								O	O	O	256
2.0–2.5		O	O	O	O	O	O														O	O	O	O	O	O	229
2.0–2.5							O	O	O	O	O	O										O	O				224
2.0–2.5							O	O	O	O	O	O											O	O			242
2.0–2.5							O	O	O	O	O	O	O	O										O	O	O	259
0.0–5.5														O	O	O	O						O	O			236
0.0–2.5						O	O	O	O	O	O										O	O					212
0.0–2.5												O	O	O	O	O	O				O	O					208
0.0–2.5	O	O																			O	O	O	O	O	O	267
0.0–2.0		O	O	O																	O	O	O	O	O	O	235
0.0–2.0				O	O	O	O														O	O	O	O	O	O	230
0.0–2.0						O	O	O	O	O	O											O	O				225
0.0–2.0												O	O	O	O	O	O					O	O				220
0.0–2.0						O	O	O	O	O	O											O	O				243
0.0–2.0												O	O	O	O	O	O					O	O				239
0.0–2.0													O	O	O	O								O	O	O	254
0.0–2.0							O	O	O	O	O	O												O	O	O	260
0.0–2.0												O	O	O	O	O								O	O	O	257

Appendix

Several Equations

The following equations are added for the convenience of those who wish to make certain supplemental calculations:

1) Calculation of *CIE chromaticity* x,y when the tristimulus values X, Y, and Z are given.

$$x = \frac{X}{X+Y+Z} \qquad y = \frac{Y}{X+Y+Z}$$

2) Calculation of the *CIE tristimulus values* when x, y, and Y are given.

$$X = \frac{x}{y} Y \qquad Z = \frac{(1-x-y)}{y} Y$$

3) Calculation of the *CIELAB color difference* ΔE^*_{ab}, when the tristimulus values X, Y, and Z are known for both colors [Ref.7.15, p. 106; 7.19,21].

$$\Delta E^*_{ab} = \sqrt{(\Delta L^*)^2 + (\Delta a^*)^2 + (\Delta b^*)^2}$$

where ΔL^*, Δa^*, and Δb^* represent the difference of L*, a*, and b*, respectively, for the two colors.

L*, a*, and b* are calculated by use of

$$L^* = 116 \left(\frac{Y}{Y_0}\right)^{1/3} - 16$$

$$a^* = 500 \left[\left(\frac{X}{X_0}\right)^{1/3} - \left(\frac{Y}{Y_0}\right)^{1/3}\right]$$

$$b^* = 200 \left[\left(\frac{Y}{Y_0}\right)^{1/3} - \left(\frac{Z}{Z_0}\right)^{1/3}\right].$$

X_0, Y_0, and Z_0 are the tristimulus values of the nominally white object-color stimulus (the illuminant). Y_0 is taken equal to 100, and X_0 and Z_0 are calculated from values of x and y for the illuminant (Table 7.6).

The formula is valid only when X/X_0, Y/Y_0, and Z/Z_0 all exceed 0.01.

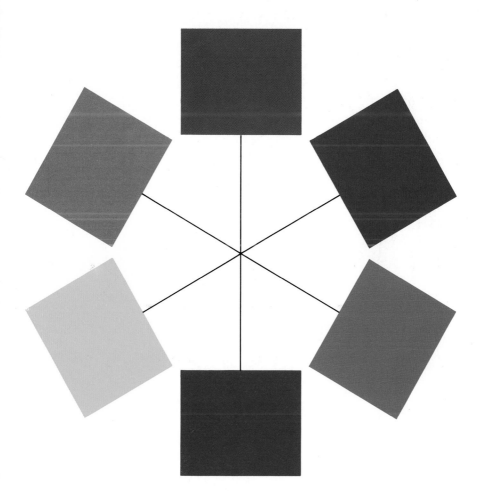

<u>Plate I.</u> Goehte color circle. The samples were cut from chips in [5.14]. The samples were photographed; hence their reproduction here must be considered only approximations of them. (cf.p.41)

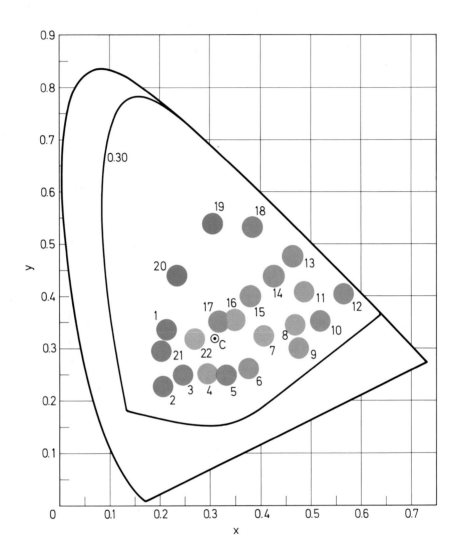

Plate II. Chromaticities of colors of samples compared with the chromaticity limits (MacAdam limits). [Luminance factor Y = 0.30 (approximately), Table 7.3]. The samples were cut from standard color chips (Munsell) and from chips in [5.14]. The samples were photographed; hence their reproduction here must be considered only approximations of them. (cf.p.68)

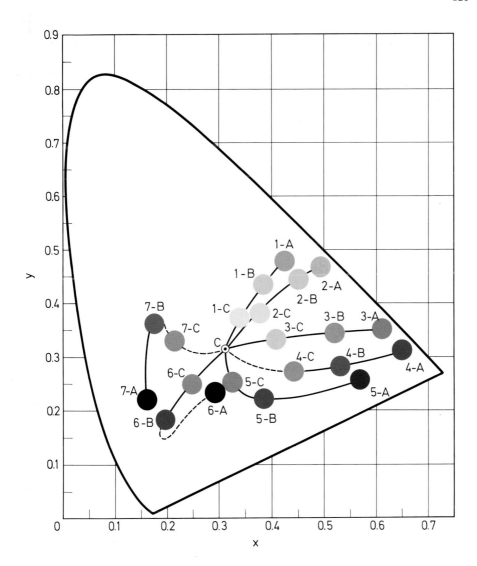

Plate III. Seven pigments and their mixtures with titanium white pigment in a paint film. Curves (mixture lines) show the variation of chromaticity with white pigment content (Table 7.4). The samples were cut from color chips in [5.14]. The samples were photographed; hence their reproduction here must be considered only approximations of them. (cf.p.71)

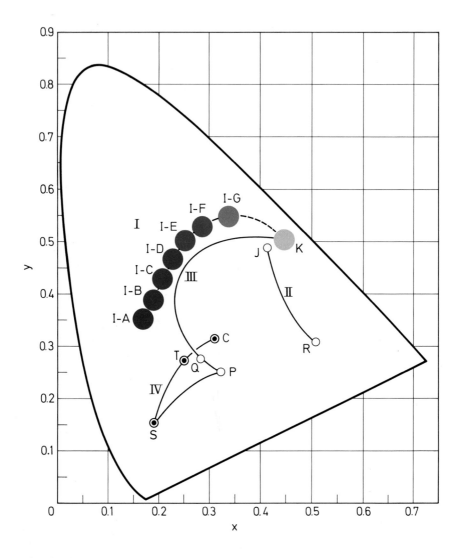

Plate IV. Mixtures of pairs of pigments in paint films. Mixture lines are shown for: (I) Milori blue and chrome yellow (K) (Table 7.5) [5.14]; (II) zinc yellow (J) and deep cadmium red (R) (reproduced from [Ref. 2.2, Fig. 18.7]); (III) Prussian blue (P) and chrome yellow (K) in oil (reproduced from [Ref. 7.12, Fig. 12]); and (IV) Prussian blue (P) and lead white (C) in oil (reproduced from [Ref. 7.12, Fig. 7]). The samples were cut from color chips in [5.14]. The samples were photographed; hence their repro-duction here must be considered only approximations of them. (cf.p. 73)

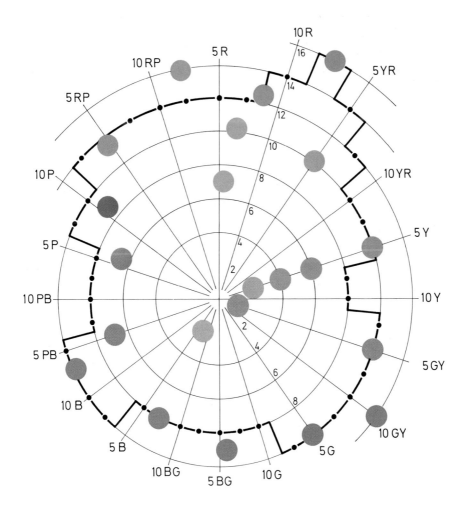

Plate V. Color samples and a line enclosing the gamut of available Munsell standard color samples at Munsell Value 6 (luminance factor Y = 0.30). The color samples displayed are the same as those in Plate II; they are de-scribed in Table 7.3. The samples were photographed; hence their reproduction here must be considered only approximations of them. (cf.p.88)

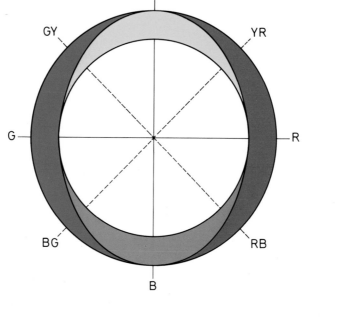

Plate VI. Hering hue circle. (Based on [Ref. 8.15, Fig. 8],cf.p. 95)

References

1.1 J.W. von Goethe: *Farbenlehre* (Color Theory)(1810). C.L. Eastlake's Translation (1940). Introduction by D.B. Judd. (M.I.T. Press, Cambridge, Mass. 1970)

1.2 R. Matthaei (ed.): *Goethe's Color Theory*. Translated by H. Aach (Van Nostrand Reinhold, New York 1970)

1.3 F. Birren: A sense of illumination. Color Res. Appl. *2*, 69-74 (1977)

1.4 A. Garrett: Report on Color 77, Third Congress of the International Color Association. Leonardo *11*, 41-42 (1978)

1.5 F. Birren: Color perception in art: Beyond the eye into the brain. Leonardo *9*, 105-110 (1976)

1.6 M.E. Chevreul: *The Principles of Harmony and Contrast of Colors and Their Applications in the Arts* (1839). Reprinted. Introduction and Notes by F. Birren (Van Nostrand Reinhold, New York 1967)

1.7 O.N. Rood: *Modern Chromatics: Students' Text-Book of Color with Applications to Art and Industry* (1879). Reprinted. Introduction and Notes by F. Birren (Van Nostrand Reinhold, New York 1973)

1.8 J. Albers: *Interaction of Color* (Yale University Press, New Haven, Conn. 1971)

1.9 J.H. Holloway, J.A. Weil: A conversation with Josef Albers. Leonardo *3*, 459-464 (1970)

1.10 D. Nickerson: History of the Munsell color system and its scientific application. J. Opt. Soc. Am. *30*, 575-586 (1940)

1.11 D. Nickerson: History of the Munsell color system. Color Eng. *7*(5), 42-51 (1969)

1.12 W. Faulkner: *Architecture and Color* (Wiley, New York 1972)

1.13 J.M. Carpenter: *Color in Art: A Tribute to Arthur Pope* (Fogg Art Museum, Harvard University, Cambridge, Mass. 1974)

1.14 A. Pope: *The Language of Drawing and Painting* (Harvard University Press, Cambridge, Mass. 1949). (Russell and Russel, New York 1967)

1.15 R.B. Farnum: Results of a questionnaire on color in art education. J. Opt. Soc. Am. *32*, 720-726 (1942)

1.16 J.T. Luke: Toward a new viewpoint for the artist. Color Res. Appl. *1*, 23-36 (1976)

1.17 G. Marcus: A color system for artists. Leonardo *9*, 48-51 (1976)

1.18 M.L. Meixner: Instruction on light and color in art at the Iowa State University. Leonardo *9*, 52-55 (1976)

1.19 L. Swirnoff: Experiments on the interaction of color and form. Leonardo *9*, 191-195 (1976)

1.20 E. Jacobson, W.C. Granville, C.E. Foss: *Color Harmony Manual*, 3rd ed. (Container Corporation of America, Chicago 1948)

1.21 *Natural Colour System (NCS) Colour Atlas* (Svenskt Färgcentrum, Stockholm)

1.22 *Munsell Book of Color*. Glossy Finish Collection and Matte Finish Collection (Munsell Color, Macbeth Division of Kollmorgen Corporation, Baltimore, Md. 1976)

2.1 R.W. Burnham, R.M. Hanes, C.J. Bartleson: *Color: A Guide to Basic Facts and Concepts* (Wiley, New York 1963)

2.2 R.M. Evans: *An Introduction to Color* (Wiley, New York 1948)

128

2.3   D.B. Judd, G. Wyszecki: *Color in Business, Science and Industry*, 3rd ed. (Wiley, New York 1975)
2.4   R.M. Evans: *The Perception of Color* (Wiley, New York 1974)
2.5   R.W.G. Hunt: "Problems in Colour Reproduction", in *Colour 73*. Second Congress of the International Colour Association, York, England (Adam Hilger, London 1973) pp. 53-75
2.6   D. Jameson, L.M. Hurvich: From contrast to assimilation: In art and in the eye. Leonardo *8*, 125-131 (1975)
2.7   E.F. MacNichol, Jr., R. Feinberg, F.I. Harosi: "Colour Discrimination Processes in the Retina", in *Colour 73*. Second Congress of the International Colour Association, York, England (Adam Hilger, London 1973) pp. 191-251
3.1   CIE (Commission Internationale de l'Eclairage), *International Lighting Vocabulary*. Publication CIE No.17 (E-1.1). (CIE, Paris 1970)
3.2   A.R. Barlee: Uniform color spaces and colorimeter performance. J. Oil Colour Chem. Assoc. *49*(4), 275-298 (1966)
3.3   J.O. Fish: *The Perception of Color* by Ralph M. Evans (Book review). Color Res. Appl. *2*, 197-199 (1977)
3.4   R.M. Evans: Fluorescence and its appearance. J. Color Appearance *1*(4), 4 (1972)
3.5   R.M. Evans: "The Perception of Color", in *Advances in Chemistry Series 107* (American Chemical Society, Washington, D.C. 1971) pp. 43-68
3.6   D.B. Judd: *The Language of Drawing and Painting* by Arthur Pope (Book review). J. Opt. Soc. Am. *40*, 122 (1950)
3.7   G. Wyszecki, W.S. Stiles: *Color Science: Concepts and Methods, Quantitative Data and Formulae* (Wiley, New York 1967)
3.8   H. Osborne (ed.): *The Oxford Companion to Art* (Oxford University Press, Oxford 1970)
4.1   S. Ostoja-Kotkowski: Audio-kinetic art with laser beams and electronic systems. Leonardo *8*, 142-144 (1975)
4.2   S. Ostoja-Kotkowski: Audio-kinetic art: The construction and operation of my "laser-chromasonic tower". Leonardo *10*, 51-53 (1977)
4.3   C.L. Strong: How to construct an argon gas laser with outputs at several wavelengths. Sci. Am. *220*(2), 118-123 (1969)
4.4   P. Sorokin: Organic lasers. Sci. Am. *220*(2), 30-40 (1969)
4.4a F.P. Schäfer (ed.): *Dye Lasers*, 2nd ed., Topics in Applied Physics, Vol. 1 (Springer, Berlin, Heidelberg, New York 1977)
4.5   F.C. Strome: The dye laser. Eastman Org. Chem. Bull. *46*(2), 1-4 (1974)
4.6   C.L. Strong: A tunable laser using organic dye is made at home for less than $75. Sci. Am. *222*(2), 116-120 (1970)
4.7   M. Bass, T.F. Deutsch, M.J. Weber: "Dye Lasers", in *Lasers*, ed. by A.K. Levine, A.J. De Maria, Vol.III (Marcel Dekker, New York 1971) p. 270
4.8   T. Kallard: *Exploring Laser Light* (Optosonic Press, New York 1977)
4.9   A.H. Taylor, G.P. Kerr: The distribution of energy in the visible spectrum of daylight. J. Opt. Soc. Am. *31*, 3-8 (1941)
4.10 OSA (Committee on Colorimetry, Optical Society of America), *The Science of Color* (T.Y. Crowell, New York 1953)
4.11 J. Beresford: Instrumental measurement of colour. J. Oil Colour Chem. Assoc. *53*(9), 800-820 (1970)
4.12 G. Wyszecki: Development of new CIE standard sources for colorimetry. *Die Farbe 19*(1-6), 43-76 (1970)
5.1   H.W. Levison: *Artists' Pigments: Lightfastness Tests and Ratings* (Colorlab, Hallandale, Florida 1976)
5.2   R. Mayer: *The Artist's Handbook of Materials and Techniques*, 3rd ed. (Thomas Nelson, London 1975)
5.3   K. Wehlte: *The Materials and Techniques of Painting* [Translated by Ursus Dix](Van Nostrand Reinhold, New York 1975)
5.4   R.J. Gettens, G.L. Stout: *Painting Materials: A Short Encyclopedia* (Dover, New York 1966)

5.5   *Colour Index* (3rd ed., revised). Research Triangle Park, N.C.: American Association of Textile Chemists and Colorists; and Bradford, Yorkshire: Society of Dyers and Colourists (1975)

5.6   E. Wich: The *Colour Index*. Color Res. Appl. *2*, 77-80 (1977)

5.7   N.F. Barnes: A spectrophotometric study of artists' pigments. Tech. Stud. Field of Fine Arts *7*(3), 120-138 (1935)

5.8   N.F. Barnes: Color characteristics of artists' pigments. J. Opt. Soc. Am. *29*(5), 208-214 (1939)

5.9   R. Bowman: Paintings with fluorescent pigments of the microcosm and macrocosm. Leonardo *6*, 289-292 (1973)

5.10 A.K. Schein, W.R. Dana: Fluorescent pigments. Paint Varn. Prod. *60*(8), 72-76 (1970)

5.11 R.W. Voedish, D.W. Ellis: Fluorescent Pigments (Daylight). *Kirk-Othmer Encyclopedia of Chemical Technology*, 2nd ed., Vol.IX (Wiley, New York 1966) pp. 483-506

5.12 R. Donaldson: Spectrophotometry of fluorescent pigments. Br. J. Appl. Phys. *5*, 210-214 (1954)

5.13 G. Wyszecki: "Current Developments in Colorimetry", in *Colour 73*. Second Congress of the International Colour Association, York, England (Adam Hilger, London 1973) pp. 21-51

5.14 Du Pont: *Pigment Colors for Paint* (revised)(E.I. du Pont de Nemours & Co., Wilmington, Del. 1957)

5.15 F. Gerritsen: "Colour Teaching: A New Colour Circle", in *Colour 73*. Second Congress of the International Colour Association, York, England (Adam Hilger, London 1973) pp. 494-498

6.1   W.D. Wright: *The Measurement of Colour*, 2nd ed. (Hilger & Watts, London 1958)

6.2   D.L. MacAdam: Color measurement and tolerances. Off. Dig. *37*(491), 1488-1531 (1965)

6.3   S.B. Saunders, F. Grum: Measurement of luminance factor. Color Res. Appl. *2*, 121-123 (1977)

6.4   D.B. Judd: "Basic Correlates of the Visual Stimulus", in *Handbook of Experimental Psychology*, ed. by S.S. Stevens (Wiley, New York 1951) Chap.22

7.1   K.L. Kelly: Color designations for lights. J. Opt. Soc. Am. *33*, 627-632 (1943)

7.2   D.L. MacAdam: On the geometry of color space. J. Franklin Inst. *238*, 195-210 (1944)

7.3   K.L. Kelly, D.B. Judd: "Color: Universal Language and Dictionary of Names"; NBS Special Publication 440 (U.S. Government Printing Office, Washington, D.C. 1976)

7.4   K.L. Kelly: Twenty-two colors of maximum contrast. Color Eng. *3*(6), 26-27 (1976)

7.5   D.L. MacAdam: Theory of the maximum visual efficiency of colored materials. J. Opt. Soc. Am. *25*, 249-252 (1935)

7.6   D. Nickerson: Light sources and color rendering. J. Opt. Soc. Am. *50*, 57-69 (1960)

7.7   D. Nickerson: Terminolgy on color rendering. J. Opt. Soc. Am. *55*, 213-214 (1965)

7.8   D.L. MacAdam: Maximum visual efficiency of colored materials. J. Opt. Soc. Am. *25*, 361-367 (1935)

7.9   M. Saltzman: Colored organic pigments: Why so many? Why so few? Off. Dig. *35*(458), 245-257 (1963)

7.10 *Modular Colors* (Trade Booklet)(Permanent Pigments, Cincinnati 1975)

7.11 *Enduring Colors for the Artist* (Permanent Pigments, Cincinnati 1975)

7.12 S.R. Jones: "The History of the Artist's Palette in Terms of Chromaticity", in *Application of Science in Examination of Works of Art*. Proceedings of Seminar (Museum of Fine Arts, Boston 1965) pp. 71-77

7.13 P.C. Goldmark, J.W. Christensen, J.J. Reeves: Color television — USA standard. Proc. I.R.E. *39*, 1288-1313 (1951)

7.14 R.S. Hunter: Instrumental methods of color and color difference measurement. Am. Ceram. Soc. Bull. *36*(7), 249-255 (1957)

7.15 S. Le Sota, et al. (compilers): *Paint/Coatings Dictionary* (Federation of Societies for Coatings Technology, Philadelphia 1978)

7.16 D.I. Morley, R. Munn, F.W. Billmeyer, Jr.: Small and moderate colour differences: II The Morley data. J. Soc. Dyers Colourists *91*, 279 (1978)

7.17 K. McLaren: The Adams-Nickerson color-difference formula. J. Soc. Dyers Colourists *86*, 354-366, 368 (1970)

7.18 K. McLaren, D.A. Plant: "ANLAB — A Uniform Colour Space for Pigment Evaluation", in *Eleventh Congress, FATIPEC* (Florence 1972) pp. 61-66

7.19 K. McLaren: The development of the CIE 1976 (L*a*b*) uniform color space and colour-difference formula. J. Soc. Dyers Colourists *92*, 338-341 (1976)

7.20 K. McLaren, B. Rigg: The SDC recommended colour-difference formula: Change to CIELAB. J. Soc. Dyers Colourists *92*, 337-338 (1976)

7.21 A.R. Robertson: The CIE 1976 color-difference formula. Color Res. Appl. *2*, 7-11 (1977)

7.22 R.F. Patrick: Applications of color difference measurements in porcelain enamels. Am. Ceram. Soc. Bull. *33*(12), 361-367 (1954)

8.1 A survey of American color specifications — 1955. Off. Dig. *28*(381), 902-921 (1956)

8.2 D. Nickerson: Interrelation of color specifications. Pap. Trade J. (TAPPI Section) *125*, 153, 219 (1947)

8.3 M.E. Bond, D. Nickerson: Color-order systems, Munsell and Ostwald. J. Opt. Soc. Am. *32*, 709-719 (1942)

8.4 C.E. Foss, D. Nickerson, W.C. Granville: An analysis of the Ostwald color system. J. Opt. Soc. Am. *34*, 361-381 (1944)

8.5 W.C. Granville, E. Jacobson: Colorimetric specification of the *Color Harmony Manual* from spectrophotometric measurements. J. Opt. Soc. Am. *34*, 382-395 (1944)

8.6 E. Jacobson: *Basic Color: An Interpretation of the Ostwald Color System* (Paul Theobald, Chicago 1948)

8.7 M. Richter: The Official German Standard Color Chart [Translated by D.B. Judd, G. Wyszecki]. J. Opt. Soc. Am. *45*, 223-226 (1955)

8.8 D. Nickerson: Horticultural colour chart names with Munsell key. J. Opt. Soc. Am. *47*, 619 (1957)

8.9 The ICI colour atlas. Paint Manuf. *40*(3), 29-30 (1970)

8.10 K. McLaren: Colour specification by visual means. J. Oil Colour Chem. Assoc. *45*, 879-886 (1971)

8.10a G.W. Haupt, J.C. Schleter, K.L. Eckerle: "The Ideal Lovibond Color System for CIE Standard Illuminants A and C Shown in Three Colorimetric Systems"; National Bureau of Standards Note 716 (1972)

8.11 A. Kornerup: The colour system in the *Methuen Handbook of Colour*. J. Oil Colour Chem. Assoc. *47*, 955-970 (1964)

8.12 Standard method for specifying color by the Munsell system (ASTM Designation D 1535-62). Off. Dig. *36*(471), 373-408 (1964)

8.13 S.M. Newhall, D. Nickerson, D.B. Judd: Final report of the OSA Subcommittee on the spacing of the Munsell colors. J. Opt. Soc. Am. *33*, 385-418 (1943)

8.14 D. Nickerson: Spacing of the Munsell colors. Illum. Eng. *40*, 373-386 (1945)

8.15 A. Hård: Philosophy of the Hering-Johansson Natural Colour System, *Proceedings of the International Colour Meeting, Lucerne 1*, 357-365 (1965); *Die Farbe 15*, 296 (1966)

8.16 A. Hård: A New Colour Atlas Based on the Natural Colour System by Hering-Johansson. *Proceedings of the International Colour Meeting, Lucerne 1*, 367-375 (1965); *Die Farbe 15*, 287 (1966)

8.17 A. Hård: Quality Attributes of Color Perception. Paper presented at Colour 69, First Congress of the International Colour Association, Stockholm (1969)

8.18 A. Hård: "The Natural Colour System and Its Universal Application in the Study of Environmental Design", in *Colour for Architecture*, ed. by T. Porter, B. Mikellides (Studio Vista, London 1975) pp. 109-119

8.19 D.B. Judd, D. Nickerson: Relations between Munsell and Swedish Natural Color System Scales. J. Opt. Soc. Am. *65*, 85-90 (1975)

8.20 D.L. MacAdam: Colorimetric data for samples of OSA uniform color scales. J. Opt. Am. *68*, 121-130 (1978); addenda, *American Institute of Physics (AIP) Document* No. PAPS JOSA-68-121-55 (1978); 570 Pages of Spectrophotometric and Colorimetric Data (6 microfiches), *Document* No. PAPS JOSA-69-206-564 (1979)

8.21 D. Nickerson: Munsell renotations for samples of the OSA Uniform Color Scales. J. Opt. Am. *68*, 1343-1347 (1978)

8.22 D. Nickerson: History of the OSA Committee on Uniform Scales. Opt. News *3*(1), 8-17 (1977)

8.23 D. Nickerson: Optical Society of America (OSA) Uniform Color Scale Samples. Leonardo *12*, 206-212 (1979)

8.24 W.E.K. Middleton: The Plochere color system: A descriptive analysis. Can. J. Res. (F) *27*, 1 (1949)

8.25 G. Reimann, D.B. Judd, H.J. Keegan: Spectrophotometric and colorimetric determination of the TCCA Standard Color Cards. J. Opt. Am. *33*, 128-159 (1946)

8.26 D. Nickerson, S.M. Newhall: A psychological color solid. J. Opt. Soc. Am. *33*, 419-423 (1943)

8.27 D.L. MacAdam: Uniform color scales. J. Opt. Soc. Am. *64*, 1691-1702 (1974)

8.28 D.L. MacAdam: "System of OSA Committee on Uniform Color Scales", in *AIC Color 77*, ed. by F.W. Billmeyer, Jr., G. Wyszecki. Third Congress of the International Colour Association, Troy, N.Y. (Adam Hilger, Bristol 1978) pp. 399-400

8.29 G. Wyszecki: A regular rhombohedral lattice sampling of Munsell renotation space. J. Opt. Soc. Am. *44*, 725-734 (1954)

8.30 G. Wyszecki: Uniform color scales: CIE 1964 U*V*W* conversion of OSA Committee selection. J. Opt. Soc. Am. *65*, 456-460 (1975)

8.31 *ISCC-NBS Centroid Color Charts*. Standard Sample No. 2016. Office of Standard Reference Materials, National Bureau of Standards, Washington, D.C. (1965)

8.32 *Webster's Third New International Dictionary* (Unabridged) (G. and C. Merriam Co., Springfield, Mass. 1971)

Author and Subject Index

134

Color contrast
  maximum 61
Color difference 75,83
Color Harmony Manual 84,94
Color limits *see* MacAdam limits
Color match 36
Color matching functions 50
Color mixture
  additive 37,44,49,61,62
  subtractive 38
  by averaging 39,61
Color-name blocks, ISCC-NBS 102
Color-name map 57,105
Color names 57,101,105
Color perception 6,9,95
Color quality 45
Color rendering 65
Color response 7,14
Color sample systems 83,84
Color scales, uniform 97
Color solid 90,93
Color space, (CIE) 81
Color specification 2,51,91
Color specification (CIE) 3,53,56,
  91
Color stimulus 7,14,15,43
Color systems 81,84
Color temperature 77
  correlated 79
Color temperature curve 77
Color terms 13
Color: Universal Languages and Dictionary of Names 102,105
Colors
  achromatic 10,58,64
  aperture 9
  centroid 61,102
  complementary 38,41,48,59,61
  chromatic 10,52

film 9
full 93
isolated 9
non-object 10
nonspectral 18,52
object 10
produced by monochromatic light
  17,52
psychological 14,81
psychophysical 14,43,45,81
related 93
spectral 18,52
surface 10
unrelated 9
Colorants 27
Colorimeter 45
Colorimetry 43
Colour Index 27
Complementary colors *see* Colors,
  complementary
Complementary wavelength 56
Cubo-octahedron 99
Culver, B. 2

Daylight 21,24
Dictionary of Colors Names see
  *Color: Universal Language and
  Dictionary of Names*
DIN-Color Chart 83,84,106
Disk, spinning 39,61
Dominant wavelength 54
Dyes 27

Electromagnetic spectrum 15
Energy, radiant 15
Equal-energy distribution 21
Equal-energy white 50
Evans, R.M. 11,12,13,14
Excitation purity *see* Purity

W. Schultze
Farbenlehre und Farbenmessung
Eine kurze Einführung
3., überarbeitete Auflage. 1975. 57 Abbildungen, davon 4 in Farbe, 3 Tabellen.
VII, 97 Seiten
ISBN 3-540-07214-4

Inhaltsübersicht:
Das Wesen der Farbe. Die Grundlagen der Farbmetrik und die Normvalenzsysteme. Die Methoden der Farbmessung und Farbbewertung. Beziehungen zwischen spektraler Energieverteilung und farbmetrischer Bewertung. Farbsammlungen, Farbordnungen und die Bewertung des Farbabstandes. Besondere Einflüsse bei der Farbbetrachung. Fluoreszenzfarben. Praktische Anwendung der Farbmetrik. Zur Frage der ästhetischen Farbbewertung.

Dye Lasers
Editor: F. P. Schäfer
2nd revised edition. 1977. 114 figures.
XI, 299 pages
(Topics in Applied Physics, Volume 1)
ISBN 3-540-08470-3

Contents:
F. P. Schäfer: Principles of Dye Laser Operation. – *B. B. Snavely:* Continuous-Wave Dye Lasers. – *C. V. Shank, E. P. Ippen:* Mode-Locking of Dye Lasers. – *K. H. Drexhage:* Structure and Properties of Laser Dyes. – *T. W. Hänsch:* Applications of Dye Lasers. – *F. P. Schäfer:* Progress in Dye Lasers: September 1973 till March 1977.

Springer-Verlag
Berlin
Heidelberg
New York

metrologia

ISSN 0026-1394   Title No. 124

International Journal of Scientific
Metrology
Published under the auspices of the
International Committee of Weights and
Measures

Editorial Board: H. Preston-Thomas,
Ottawa; E. R. Cohen, Thousand Oaks, CA;
P. Dean, Middlesex; T. W. Hânsch, Stan-
ford, CA; B. N. Taylor, Washington, DC;
G. W. Wyszecki, Ottawa.

Advisory Board: V. O. Arontunov, Lenin-
grad; J. de Boer, Amsterdam;
G. D. Bourdoun, Moskow; L. E. Howlett,
Ottawa; F. J. Lehany, Chippendale;
J. M. Otero, Madrid; L. Plaza, Madrid;
J. Stulla-Götz, Vienna; J. Terrien, Sevres;
Y. Tomonaga, Tokyo; M. S. Vallarta,
Mexico City; Z. Yamauti, Tokyo

Springer-Verlag
Berlin
Heidelberg
New York

Metrologia reports research dealing with the
improvement of basic measurements in
physics. Emphasis is on the refinement of
the six units that comprise the International
System of Units – meter, kilogram, second,
ampere, degree, and candela.

Sample copies and subscription
information upon request.